A YEAR'S LETTERS

The publication of this work has been aided by a grant from
The Andrew W. Mellon Foundation

MR ALGERNON SWINBURNE

A YEAR'S LETTERS

by

Algernon Charles Swinburne

―――――――

edited by

Francis Jacques Sypher

NEW YORK: NEW YORK UNIVERSITY PRESS

1974

ISBN: 8147-7758-9
Library of Congress Catalog Card No: 74-15290

Manufactured in the United States of America

To
M.A.S.
New joy wait on you!

Contents

List of Illustrations   viii

Acknowledgments   ix

Introduction.   xi

To the Author   1

A Year's Letters   5

Textual Notes   167

Explanatory Notes.   179

List of Illustrations

Swinburne's *carte de visite*
  (Harvard College Library) . . . . *frontispiece*

Capheaton, Northumberland. Drawn by Miss E. Swin-
  burne [Swinburne's aunt]. Engraved by W. R. Smith
  (Neale's *Views of the Seats of Noblemen and Gentlemen*,
  London, 1822)   xiii

The Virgin Crowned, San Zanipolo, Venice: in letter 27
  Redgie tells Clara of the portrait head of her in the
  right corner—only with "thick curled gold hair"
  (Anderson—Art Reference Bureau)   xv

"Kirklowes," MS. Ashley 5257, folio 1^v
  (British Library)   xxii

A Year's Letters, MS. Ashley 5073, folio 4^r
  (British Library)   xxvi

Acknowledgments

It is a pleasure to acknowledge the generous encouragement and advice of Mr. John S. Mayfield, Professor Cecil Y. Lang, Mr. T. A. J. Burnett, and Professor C. K. Hyder. I am grateful to the British Library, the Harvard College Library, and the Rutgers University Library for permission to use unpublished manuscripts, and for many courtesies during my visits to their collections. And I must thank William Heinemann Ltd. for permission to print unpublished work by Swinburne. Mr. Edwin E. Williams, Professor Hugh Maclean, and Professor Donald Prakken gave welcome suggestions. For help of many sorts, thanks are due to the officers and staff of New York University Press.

Introduction

I

The moral climate of the Victorian age did not favor the kind of story Swinburne had to tell. The "British matron" (male or female), whose interests were powerfully represented in the press and in the subscription lists of the great circulating libraries, wished to read nothing that would bring a blush to the cheek of a young person. Meredith's *Ordeal of Richard Feverel* was condemned, and George Eliot's *The Mill on the Floss* regarded as a dangerous book. Hardy struggled throughout his career as a novelist against censorship of his books and charges of immorality until the outcry over *Jude the Obscure* caused him to abandon fiction altogether. In such an atmosphere it is unimaginable that Swinburne's tales of adultery and flagellation could ever have been tolerated, much less encouraged.

But he did have a story, and, like the ancient mariner, a need to tell it. He did not publish his novel under his own name until 1905 (in a twice censored version), forty-three years after he wrote it; but in the meantime he gave the public reworkings of Greek tragedy, of medieval legend, and of modern history, and wove them into a rich literary production in an impressive variety of forms. An early commentator opined that he could see no "internal center" in Swinburne's work—presumably in this view all his versatility was the result of a certain nervous energy which expended itself indiscriminately on whatever subject came to hand. But a full view of Swinburne's writings conveys precisely the opposite impression. The center is there, always perceptible, exerting its power over every line. The problem is that it takes on such dazzlingly various aspects that it evades definition. Meleager and Tristram, Mary Stuart and Lucrezia Borgia, Lady

Midhurst and Dolores, are real persons for Swinburne. They are actors in one complex drama, filled with guilt and mystery, with aspirations and losses, passionate loves and hatreds. Each of them has his point of origin in the "internal center"; the difficulty is to penetrate the disguises. One of the great attractions of *A Year's Letters* is that in this novel, one feels so close to the undisguised center of Swinburne's genius.

A Year's Letters is densely autobiographical. In the first instance, Redgie Harewood is a clear double for Algie (or Hadji, as he was known *en famille*) Swinburne. Swinburne's family had lived for centuries in Northumberland, where Sir John Swinburne (the poet's grandfather) had his seat, Capheaton—the model for the fictional Lidcombe—with its "admirable slopes of high bright hill-country behind it, and green sweet miles of park and embayed lake, beyond praise for riding or boating." Apart from regular visits to his grandfather's, Swinburne grew up at Bonchurch, on the Isle of Wight, where his father, Admiral Charles Henry Swinburne (Sir John Swinburne's second son) had near the sea a long, many-chimneyed house, which has since become a convent. A maze of consanguineous relations brought Swinburne together with cousins like Mary Gordon, who described the connection with the adroitness of an expert in family matters: "Our mothers (daughters of the third Earl of Ashburnham) were sisters; our fathers, first cousins—more alike in characters and tastes, more linked in closest friendship, than many brothers. Added to this, our paternal grandmothers—two sisters and co-heiresses—were first cousins to our common maternal grandmother; thus our fathers were also second cousins to their wives before marriage." [1] The children would spend their time riding ponies by the sea, or through the Northumbrian fields, reciting poetry to one another, playing bouts rimés, and writing and performing plays and tableaux, in one of which Hadji

[1] *The Boyhood of Algernon Charles Swinburne: Personal Recollections by his Cousin Mrs. Disney Leith* [Mary Gordon] (London, 1917), p. 3. There is a photograph of the house at Bonchurch, facing p. 6.

Drawn by Miss F. Swinburne.

Engraved by W.R. Smith.

CAPHEATON.

NORTHUMBERLAND.

took the part of Dickens's disreputable Mrs. Skewton in her Bath chair.

Like Redgie, Swinburne went to school—to Eton, that is —where the then prevailing system of corporal punishment was applied with lasting impression upon him. Even years later when he was respectably secluded in the London suburb of Putney, he relived—in the fictional persons of Arthur or Edmund or Willie or Frank—the agonies of the flogging block. And there are indications that he on occasion actually had the ceremonies re-enacted upon him. His greatest love at school was reading the early English drama—which was not part of the regular work. His cousin Lord Redesdale remembered him "sitting perched up Turk- or tailor-wise in one of the windows looking out on the yard, with some huge old-world tome, almost as big as himself, upon his lap, the afternoon sun setting on fire the great mop of red hair." [2]

Again like Redgie, Swinburne went to Oxford, which he left in 1860 under an obscure cloud, without taking his degree. There he became a confirmed enthusiast in the creed of revolution, as preached by Aurelio Saffi and Giuseppe Mazzini. There too, Swinburne began in earnest his poetic apprenticeship—the results of which were to startle the literary world in 1865 and 1866, when *Atalanta in Calydon* and *Poems and Ballads* appeared.

Unluckily—or perhaps it is just as well—we know of Swinburne's early love affairs little except what can be surmised from his literary works and from a few hints elsewhere. Perhaps he, like Redgie, had a *grand amour* with a married cousin. Mary Gordon is a persuasive candidate for the role of Swinburne's "lost love"—but it is difficult to say to what extent the fictional Clara might resemble her. As for the other liaison in the story— between Redgie's sister Amy (married to her cousin Lord Cheyne), and Clara's (unmarried) brother Frank—we have even

[2] "Swinburne at Eton," in *The Life of Algernon Charles Swinburne* by Sir Edmund Gosse, in the "Bonchurch Edition" of Swinburne's *Complete Works* (London and New York, 1927), XIX, 291.

The Virgin Crowned, San Zanipolo, Venice: in letter 27 Redgie tells Clara of the portrait head of her in the right corner—only with "thick curled gold hair."

less to go on in searching out possible biographical parallels. And, according to Swinburne at least, Lady Midhurst—Redgie's grandmother—is entirely his own invention.

Aside from the matter of parallels there is another, deeper way in which *A Year's Letters* is autobiographical. Nearly every theme of Swinburne's writing (which includes his own letters) is touched upon; for example: love, romantic idealism, hero-worship, revolutionary politics, religious skepticism, Stoicism, sadism, flagellation, incest, love of babies, anti-sentimentality, social satire, antiquarianism, snobbery, family loyalty, family hatred, painting, Francophilia, games, bravery, chivalry, poetry, literary criticism . . . a full list with appropriate discussions could be titled, Sorbonne style, "Swinburne, sa vie et son œuvre." This is why one feels so close to Swinburne's "internal center" as one reads *A Year's Letters*. And perhaps this is a reason that Swinburne himself kept going back to the same material to compose unpublishable studies of contemporary life and manners like his unfinished and untitled sequel, the *étude à la Balzac* known as *Lesbia Brandon*. He did publish a drama, *The Sisters* (1892), with the familiar company of young kinsfolk mixed in tangles of hopeless love, and presided over by cool seniors. But the play, remarkable as it is, especially in its molding of colloquial speech into the confines of blank verse, is too terse to allow the sort of character development that Swinburne accomplished so brilliantly in his finished novel.

The brilliant finish of *A Year's Letters* is the result of Swinburne's skillful handling of the epistolary form. In most novels of the sort, the author's narrative frets at the limits of probable correspondence. Even Laclos in *Les Liaisons dangereuses* sometimes slips into narrative. But Swinburne had as models not only epistolary novels, but real letters, like those of Mme de Sévigné; or memoirs, like those of the duc de Saint-Simon. Like them, *A Year's Letters* is rich with the texture of contemporary events—political, artistic, and literary. And we know from Swinburne's own correspondence that he was a master of the letter as a literary form. To understand the characters in *A Year's Letters*, one must attend to the patterns of persuasion and digression in the letters, their delicate tonal strokes; yet their language is pleasantly (and deceivingly) simple in phrasing, diction, and even punctuation. Redgie occasionally breaks into fervent lyricism, but he, after all, is a poet. In any case, the letters are as far as one could wish from the *prose* of most nineteenth-century novelists.

Each correspondent has a distinctive style—*ancien régime* (Lady Midhurst), muscular Christian (Redgie's father, Captain Harewood), schoolboy-intense (Redgie); and they vary their tactics to suit the requirements of their situation and the sensibilities of their correspondent. A further complication—especially with Lady Midhurst's ironic letters, and to some extent with Clara's sentimental ones—is that the directions in the letter may be meant to be obeyed or disobeyed. Lady Midhurst admits that she is expert in applying reverse psychology.

Lady Midhurst is the presiding spirit of *A Year's Letters*. She watches over her grandchildren and niece and nephew as they play out their love game, and she controls and directs almost their every move. From her letters emerges the portrait of a personality both rational and passionate, prejudiced but not reckless, cruel and kind, and eagerly artistic. She has a weakness for the manners of the eighteenth century (she was born in its last year). She is an informed and accurate judge of literature, and a published author (her satiric sketch in the mythical *Timon*). And she projects her fantasies into unwritten novels. Her best works of art are made not in print, but in life. The marriage of her daughter, the elder Amicia, to Captain Harewood, and her divorce and remarriage to Frederick Stanford were Lady Midhurst's deliberate constructions. Her character is perfectly anticipated by the marquise de Merteuil in *Les Liaisons dangereuses* when she comments on Valmont's remark that the older women get, the more they become "rêches et sévères." A small class—

rare, mais véritablement précieuse, est celle des femmes qui, ayant eu un caractère et n'ayant pas négligé de nourrir leur raison, savent se créer une existence, quand celle de la nature leur manque; et prennent le parti de mettre à leur esprit les pompons qu'elles employaient avant pour leur figure. Celles-ci ont pour l'ordinaire le jugement très sain, et l'esprit à la fois solide, gai et gracieux. Elles remplacent les charmes séduisants par l'attachante bonté, et encore par l'enjouement dont le charme augmente en proportion de l'âge: c'est ainsi qu'elles parviennent en quelque sorte à se rapprocher de la jeunesse en s'en faisant aimer. Mais alors, loin d'être, comme vous le dites, *rêches et sévères,* l'habitude de l'indulgence, leurs longues réflexions sur la faiblesse humaine, et enfin les souvenirs de leur jeunesse, par lesquels seuls elles tiennent encore à la vie, les placeraient plutôt, peut-être, trop près de la facilité. (Lettre 113.)

Lady Midhurst's *souvenirs de sa jeunesse* inspire her attraction to Redgie. And her memory of compromises and lost opportunities provides the text for her Stoic sermons to Clara and Amicia. The more one reads her letters, the more one sees in them hints and suggestions of the events and passions of a whole lifetime. There is the material for a dozen novels implicit in *A Year's Letters.*

In his "Prologue" to the letters, Swinburne carefully defines the social world of the story, which he regarded as, among other things, an exercise in scientific realism. He sharply portrays the class rivalry between Lady Midhurst and her niece, Clara. Lady Midhurst's brother, John Cheyne, had run through his money and married a certain Miss Banks, of undistinguished lineage, respectable means, and irritating manners, which she has bequeathed in different measure to her children, Frank and Clara. Clara tried to get at the title through the affections of her cousin, Edmund, the eldest son of old Lord Cheyne; but Lady Midhurst blocked this plan, and instead saw that the heir married her granddaughter, Amy. In the course of the year or so covered by this correspondence Lady Midhurst, with the help of some admirable luck, keeps the title on her side again. Lord Cheyne, the "philanthropist," after three years of marriage to Amy has no children. His duty is taken up by Frank, and when poor Edmund drowns accidentally Frank gains the title for only a few months before being disinherited by the healthy male offspring of his liaison. In her last letter, Lady Midhurst exults in her victory and in the retreat from the field of the children of her stupid brother John and Miss Banks. The success of the Cheynes lies, one imagines, in their ability to produce every few generations someone like Lady Midhurst who can keep the members of the family in place. Examples abound of families, like Mr. Chetwood's, who had not such luck.

Redgie's flagellation stories in the "Prologue" are apt to make readers uneasy, although they are doubtless taken from life, and the like might be heard in many a most respectable boys' school today. But sadism is an essential part of Swinburne's view of nature and human experience. Redgie's cruel punishment at school is a preparation for his suffering at the hands of fate, whose agent is Lady Midhurst. He and she are complementary, and sympathetic to one another. His hero-worship is inversely related to his rebelliousness. He stands up to unworthy antagonists, but he takes a kind of sensual pleasure in kneeling down before his betters. He is proud, brave, fearless; yet he thrills at the sting of submission—to a mistress, a hero, a cause, or an idea. He has in him the complex makings of a hero and martyr.

The action of *A Year's Letters* is comic, in spite of occasional rumblings which threaten to turn it to the "tearful style." In her last letter Lady Midhurst writes that but for Edmund's death and the birth of Amy's child everything is as it was: *"Le dénouement c'est qu'il n'y a pas de dénouement."* But everything is also greatly changed. Clara and Frank have been removed from the scene, and Redgie and Amy have been through their first love affairs. The developments of the story are less in actions than in attitudes. It is proof of a powerful faculty for detached analysis that Swinburne at the age of about twenty-five could see himself as Redgie through the mercilessly sympathetic eyes of Lady Midhurst. But the comic spirit radiates its light even wider. Victorian notions of humanitarianism, sentimental idealism, and scientific progress, are severally laid bare under the edge of Lady Midhurst's anatomizing wit. She is impressively fresh by comparison to the tepidly righteous Clara, the blandly philanthropic Edmund, and the dryly scientific Ernest. But her clarity of view is achieved at the expense of the reverse quality that makes Redgie so appealing—that capacity for insane dedication without which there would be no lovers or poets in the world.

Swinburne's novel was too daring to find a sympathetic audience in its day. His fictional representation of adultery and flagellation, his subtlety of style, and his too truthfully unconventional characters would have been offensive to Victorian readers. Perhaps in these respects his novel will now be more likely to attract than to repel. But it will not be denied that his satire of laborious science, of placid philanthropy, and of moral hypocrisies and sentimentalities of all sorts, is at least as pertinent today as it was in 1862.

II

Swinburne three times gives the date when he composed *A Year's Letters*. Writing to W. M. Rossetti on March 20, 1866, he called the novel his "first attempt at serious prose work, perpetrated in '62." On February 14, 1877, he wrote to Theodore Watts of his "maiden attempt (in 1862–3) at a study of contemporary life and manners." And in a letter to his sister, Isabel, June 21, 1905, Swinburne said that the letters were "dated just about the time I wrote them or perhaps a year earlier." He was probably working on the novel at the time he signed himself "Redgie" in a letter to his companion connoisseur in the mysteries of the rod, R. M. Milnes, November 13, 1862. These letters and others quoted below, are printed in Cecil Y. Lang's edition of *The Swinburne Letters*, 6 vols. (New Haven, 1959–1962).

A Year's Letters was Swinburne's first attempt at "serious" prose work: but it was preceded by his farcical French novel, *La Fille du Policeman*, written in 1860 and 1861; and followed by

Lesbia Brandon, which was begun around 1864. The relatively immature narrative fragments headed "Kirklowes" were probably written before he began to plan *A Year's Letters.*[3] In this story, of which only a few pages are known, there is a man named Harewood whose chief recreations are reading the Bible and flogging his son Reginald. Reginald's sister Eleanor is an amoral sensualist who feeds "with a soft sensual relish on the sight or conceit of physical pain," and therefore enjoys her brother's torments. She marries one Frederick Ashurst but runs off with a Mr. Champneys, whose drowning in a Channel squall is described in horribly close detail. The names and events are akin to those of *A Year's Letters,* but in manner the stories are quite different. The early narrative is awkwardly written and thoroughly sinister; in the novel, the element of cruel sensuality is tempered with a welcome addition of comic spirit and finished style.

It would seem that as Swinburne was writing out this early story he was already beginning to plan *A Year's Letters,* for on the back of the first leaf he made some random jottings of names that he used in the novel: Reginald Harewood, Ernest [Radworth], Arthur [Lunsford], Frank [Cheyne], Edmund [Cheyne]. With these are cryptic notes that suggest other projects of related inspiration: the phrase "Never any more while I live" not only is the first line of Browning's poem, "In a Year," but it echoes Lady Wariston in *Lesbia Brandon* (ch. xv)—"Never while we live any more"; the name "Edmund Hazlehurst" appears in a tantalizingly obscure (and unpublished) dramatic fragment; and the name "Lucrezia Estense Borgia" refers to a projected work of which unpublished fragments survive, as well as *The Duke of Gandia* (1908).[4]

[3] MS. Ashley 5257, British Library (where T. J. Wise's Ashley Library now resides). Printed by Randolph Hughes in his edition of *Lesbia Brandon* (London, 1952), pp. 171–180; also in *The Novels of A. C. Swinburne,* with an introduction by Edmund Wilson (New York, 1962), pp. 357–366.

[4] The dramatic fragment is in a MS. in the Mitchell Library, Library of New South Wales, Sydney, Australia (Randolph Hughes papers, Vol. MS. MSS 671/51, pp. 29–50). On L. E. B. see Swinburne's letter of January 19, 1861, in which he uses the language of Mrs. Gamp to express his enthusiasm about her. See also his *Lucretia*

a religious & torpid old woman who had just energy enough to [...] in her self; Mr. [...], her brother, an [...] [...] man with sharp eyes; & a rather singular French lady, who [...] Mrs. [...]'s companion & [...] who [...] the last six years.

Reginald

Etsi
me
[...]

Reginald Hareword
Ernest
Arthur
Frank
Edmund

After death
Et
me E PR
New

Edmund Hazlehurst
Et q quer

Lucrezia
Estense
Borgia

Never any more Wildeline

LD

"Kirklowes," MS. Ashley 5257, folio 1ᵛ.

Some other scraps of manuscript show that Swinburne made careful plans before he composed *A Year's Letters.* He wrote out a table of contents which (except for the omission of the letter "To the Author") corresponds to the arrangement of the final novel.[5] Cancellations in the list indicate that he considered having letter 14 written to Reginald from Lady Cheyne rather than Lady Midhurst; and letter 20 was first conceived as from Reginald to Mrs. Radworth. Over letter 28 is the tentative suggestion ("? R.H.") that Lady Midhurst's letter breaking off the relation between Clara and Redgie might have been directed to Reginald rather than to Clara. On the margin of the leaf is a tabulation of the number of letters written by each correspondent. On the other side of the same leaf is the text of Swinburne's French prefatory note to "Laus Veneris," and in the lower margin some names for characters in *A Year's Letters:* Chavernais, Castigny, Saverny, Chaverny, Savigny, Villenoire, Savignac, Villenier, Ville, Faringdon, Fotherington. The last nine are crossed out. Of all these names only the following were actually used: Castigny (the maiden name of Mme de Rochelais), Saverny (Octave de, the onetime friend of Clara), and Fotherington (Lord and Lady, with whom Redgie is to study the arts of diplomacy).

The most valuable of the preliminary notes for the novel is an outline fragment, in which Swinburne made quick sure indications of the contents and style of each letter.[6] His only later changes seem to have been in the dates and in the name of M. de Saverny. The fragment is worth giving here in full:

Borgia: The Chronicle of Tebaldeo Tebaldei, commentary and notes by Randolph Hughes (London, 1942).

[5] In the Swinburne Collection of Edith S. and John S. Mayfield, MS. No. 219. The paper is watermarked 1862.

[6] MS. Ashley A1851. On the reverse of the leaf is a draft of a poem headed "A Match—Stage Play—Stage Love." The paper has no watermark date. The outline was quoted in part by Georges Lafourcade, *La Jeunesse de Swinburne* (Paris, 1928), II, 289, and reproduced in full by J. O. Jordan in his dissertation, "The Novels of Algernon C. Swinburne," Stanford University, 1968, pp. 20–21, and 187.

21. Ly M. writes to give a bad account of A. plays her cards agst the Rochelais alliance. Victor de Saverny. Reginald's prospects. Would Mlle de R. do for him? Could not Frank & the Radworths return to Lidcombe for the autumn & winter? Or visit Lord Charnworth? Dim hint of dawning kid.

[2]2. Capt. H. desires Redgie to get to work. No Radworth visiting. Row about C. R. Summary of Redgie's character & conduct. Moral & religious blow-up. Style muscular-Xtian.

23. Frank to Clara. Anti-matrimonial. Reverts to Amicia. Has heard about Reginald. Pas de ça, Lisette.

24. Thanks for things sent from Lidcombe. Sorry about Redgie. Hopes well. Glad if Frank should marry. Is ill.

25. Anti-filial. Account of interview with Clara. Will not
Nov. give up. Abject atrocities of the osteologist. Ruat cœlum. Style Cecco.

26. Appeals for all their sakes. Her own evil case. Ly M.
[D]ec. ill with worry. What the Rochelais says of Clara & Victor de Saverny. He must be good & remember things. Touches on duties & feelings. &c. Mrs. Stanford.

27. Is waiting; let her give him the word. Rhapsodizes.

28. Announces advent of A.'s kid: a boy. Remarks at
Feb. large. Intimates that if she sees Redgie again, or does not write under dictation, he will be shewn the Saverny correspondance. Desinit in piscem. Style bland-savage, dashed with satiric virtue.

[2]9. Is leaving Lidcombe for Blocksham: agrees not to see Amy. Clara dead beat, but safe; viciously resigned. Ashamed of the business. Thanks Ly M. for helping to break it up so as to save reputations.

[3]0. Writes from Lidcombe to Ashton Hildred. Pleased
with F. Interview with Reginald, who has got his
quietus from C. administered in the resolute martyr
li[ne . . . .

The full manuscript of *A Year's Letters* appears, as one would
expect after such careful planning, to have been written out easily,
and with relatively little revision. Of the sheets with watermark
dates, thirty-seven have 1862, and two have 1860: the sheets of
the prefatory letter "To the Author" are on paper of a slightly
different color, and one of them is marked 1866, which suggests
that the letter may have been an afterthought (it is not included in
the outline of contents mentioned above), prompted by letters of
rejection which Swinburne received when he first submitted the
manuscript for publication, and perhaps also by the reviewers'
outcry over his *Poems and Ballads* (1866).

As early as 1863, Swinburne sent the novel to several publishers, none of whom would look at it. J. B. Payne, of Moxon's,
who had brought out *Atalanta in Calydon* in 1865, refused *A Year's
Letters* when it was submitted to him in 1865 or 1866. And neither
W. M. Rossetti nor Joseph Knight, whom Swinburne had asked to
sponsor his unwanted offspring, could find a place for it.[7] The
problems were several. The representation of adulterous love
affairs was a strong stroke against the book. But worst of all,
Swinburne, for reasons not altogether clear, did not wish to have
his name associated with it. His oral arrangement with Payne had
been to send "without my name and without in any way commit-
ting myself to their authorship, MSS which I should wish you to
print as though they were avowedly or probably mine." [8] There is
a characteristic pattern in Swinburne's love of disguise and pseud-
onymity. But in the particular case of *A Year's Letters,* one

[7] See *Letters*, III, 251; I, 155–156, 158, 162, 169. Knight's letter, Feb. 25, 1866 (MS.
Ashley A1941) was printed in T. J. Wise's *A Swinburne Library* (London, 1925), pp.
173–174.

[8] *Letters*, I, 156.

1.
Prologue

In the spring of 1849, old Lord Ancyne, the noted philanthropist,
was, it will be remembered by all those interested in social reform,
still alive & energetic. Indeed he had some nine years of active
life before him. Public baths, institutes, reading-rooms, schools,
lecture-halls, all manner of improvements, bore witness to his ardour
in the cause of humanity. The equable eye of philosophy has
long since observed that the appetite of doing good, unlike those
baser appetites which time effaces & enjoyment allays, gains in strength
& vigour with advancing years. A cheering truth, the
life & death of this excellent man would alone suffice to
for one of his admirable plans was ever known to miss. Re-
-ciprocal amelioration, he was wont to say, was the aim of
every acquaintance he made — of every act of benevolence he allowed
himself. Religion alone was wanting to complete a character almost
painfully perfect. The mutual moral friction of benefits bestowed
& blessings received had as it were rubbed off the edge of those qualities
which go to make up the religious sentiment. The spiritual cuticle of
this truly so good man was so hardened by the incessant titillations of charity
& of that complacency with which virtuous people look back on days
well spent, that the nervous emotions of faithful piety had no
on it, no tickling of doctrine or devotion could excite his fancy or his
faith. At least no clearer reason than this has yet been assigned
in explanation of a fact so lamentable.

His son Edmund, the late lord, whose regretted decease is yet fresh
in the memory of a large & sorrowing circle of friends, was

wonders if there were not also more direct reasons for his wishing to conceal his authorship. Perhaps certain incidents and characters were too recognizably drawn from the author's own experience, and might have caused embarrassment in certain quarters.

After the controversy over the immorality of *Poems and Ballads* in 1866, Payne refused to sponsor Swinburne's books any further, and his accounts were transferred to John Camden Hotten, who had a varied list of titles, and no reputation to lose by bringing out scandalous poems. *A Year's Letters* was offered to Hotten, but according to W. M. Rossetti, "he, thinking it would make little or no impression if anonymous, declined." [9] At the time of this entry in his journal, January 25, 1869, W. M. R. was under the impression that the novel was to be brought out anonymously in America.

The projected American publication was spoken of by Swinburne's shadowy friend, John Thomson, to the American poet, Bayard Taylor, who was in London in 1868. Taylor took back to the United States a copy of the novel (probably the transcript referred to by Swinburne in his letter of March 10 [1868]) [10] and discussed it with one of his literary cronies, R. H. Stoddard. The MS. was to be submitted to Lippincott, who expressed himself "willing to publish the novel anonymously," provided he found "nothing in it intrinsically objectionable." [11] For reasons not hard to guess, nothing came of this venture, and Swinburne did not publish his novel until nine years later.

Thomas Purnell, at whose house Swinburne had met Giuseppe Mazzini, asked him in 1876 if he would submit *A Year's Letters* for publication in a new journal, *The Tatler*. Swinburne on December 27 answered his request with reports of excited exclamations on

[9] *Rossetti Papers: 1862 to 1870* (London, 1903), p. 380.

[10] *Letters,* II, 139. Swinburne's letter to Thomson is printed with the date [?1871]; but 1868 fits more neatly.

[11] Taylor's letter to Stoddard, dated Sept. 28, 1868 (Cornell University, Dept. of MSS., No. 14/18/1169) is partially printed by Richard Cary, *The Genteel Circle: Bayard Taylor and his New York Friends* (Ithaca, New York, 1952), p. 34. Taylor's letter to Swinburne, Oct. 31, 1868, is printed in Wise's *Bibliography of . . . Swinburne* (London, 1920, reprinted 1966), II, 395.

the part of his "friend," Mrs. Horace Manners, the nominal authoress of *A Year's Letters*, whose relation to Swinburne parallels that of Mrs. Harris to Mrs. Gamp in *Martin Chuzzlewit*.[12] But he asked for time to see what sort of thing the new journal would turn out to be, and meanwhile sent the MS. to his friend and former college mentor, John Nichol, for him to look it over and give his advice. Nichol praised generously, making a curious comparison with an American novel which has in common with Swinburne's only that it treats of adultery and that its title has the word "letter" in it. Nichol also marked in green pencil his suggestions for excisions (mostly of flagellation passages). Swinburne went over the MS. accepting and rejecting Nichol's suggested deletions, and making a few significant additions, and many minor changes of his own, and forwarded Mrs. Horace with "a few specks brushed from her garments, and a drop or two of strengthening medicine administered to the fair traveller."[13]

Theodore Watts, who even at this time was taking the overseer's view of his friend's affairs, expressed some anxiety about the character of the novel and of *The Tatler*, either of which might not in his eye add to Swinburne's reputation in the world of respectable letters. But Swinburne soothed the dragon in a diplomatically worded epistle of February 14, 1877, and at once began arranging with Purnell for publication.

The first issues of *The Tatler* came out in February 1877; and the editor, R. E. Francillon, wrote Swinburne on August 7 to tell of his pride and pleasure in having *A Year's Letters*.[14] The novel

[12] See *Letters*, III, 244–245. Julian Hawthorne helped start *The Tatler*, and tells a story which is good enough to quote, but almost too good to be credible: the novel "was to be printed, he insisted, if printed at all, under the name of Mrs. Horace Mann: though afterward, when we represented that a woman of that name already existed, the widow of a famous American educationist, and, in fact, an aunt of my own, the poet consented to so far modify the pseudonym as to make it Mrs. Horace Manners"; *The Memoirs of Julian Hawthorne*, edited by his wife, Edith Garrigues Hawthorne (New York, 1938), p. 226.

[13] *Letters*, III, 274–275. See Nichol's letters of Jan. 22 and Jan. 28, 1877, partially printed in Wise's *A Swinburne Library*, pp. 174–175.

[14] Transcript (on "The Pines" letterhead, and not in R. E. F.'s hand) of a letter from Francillon to Swinburne, in the Mayfield Collection.

was to begin with the first number of the new series, on August 25. But Francillon's pleasant expectations were disappointed on three counts. Swinburne insisted that his name not be used, not even be allowed to "ooze out" (he strongly complained about a note in the "Literary Gossip" column of the *Athenæum* for August 25, in which he was named as the author);[15] he declined Francillon's invitation to become a contributor and instead emphatically demanded payment after the novel and the journal had both run out;[16] finally, and worst of all, the novel, which in any case was an unlikely candidate for serial publication, did not, under the name of Mrs. Horace Manners, save the journal from extinction: "Who cared to pay threepence a week for a new serial in a new paper by a new authoress of whom nobody had ever heard?"[17] There is some indication that a few persons at least heard something. W. M. Rossetti on October 23 [1877] wrote Swinburne that he had been reading the novel: "Is it making a sensation? I found the shopkeeper of whom I bought Part 1 of Tatler knew that it was 'Swinburne's novel.'"[18] And an unidentified correspondent who had heard of Swinburne's fictional efforts asked if he would "make an offer" of a novel for publication. Swinburne, carefully guarding his words, replied: "I happen *not* to have written a novel lately."[19] One cannot help wondering all the more about his insistence in concealing his attempts at fiction. According to Francillon, his

[15] *Athenæum* [vol. 70] No. 2600 (Aug. 25, 1877); p. 227 has an announcement of the appearance of the novel, and the bit of gossip is on p. 235. Swinburne protested, and Francillon's answer, directed to Theodore Watts, August 30, 1877, is in the British Library (MS. Ashley A5076). The note from the *Athenæum* was also printed in *The Times*, Aug. 25, 1877, p. 6, col. 4. A paragraph on Swinburne and his novel appeared in the New York *Daily Tribune*, Sept. 6, 1877, p. 4, col. 5.

[16] On the subject of Swinburne's claims against *The Tatler*, letters survive from Francillon, Watts, and L. D. Powles, who was legally responsible for the debts of the journal; in May 1878 he settled the account by paying £45 of the £88 that was originally due (MSS. Ashley A5076).

[17] R. E. Francillon, *Mid-Victorian Memories* (London and New York, 1914), p. 235.

[18] MS. Ashley A1941; quoted in Wise's *A Swinburne Library* (London, 1925), p. 175.

[19] *Letters*, IV, 20.

argument was, in effect, *sic volo, sic jubeo; stet pro ratione voluntas.*

For some years after her debut in *The Tatler,* Mrs. Horace led a sheltered life. But she seems to have been kept in memory by a small circle of admirers, and she was given select publicity by two bibliographers, R. H. Shepherd, and T. J. Wise.[20] Her fame was alive in America, where in Portland, Maine, T. B. Mosher in 1901 brought out a small, unauthorized edition of *A Year's Letters*—with Swinburne's name on the title page. According to the preface, he made his reprint from "a copy of *The Tatler* formerly owned by Frederick Locker-Lampson," who knew Swinburne and had seen the MS. of the novel.[21]

A copy of this edition eventually came into Swinburne's hands, and Watts-Dunton (as he now styled himself), perhaps anxious about the copyright, persuaded him to republish it. He still felt awkward about the book which, as he wrote in the "Dedication," "would never have revisited the light or rather the twilight of publicity under honest and legitimate auspices, if it had not found in you a sponsor and a friend." But relations between the piratical Mosher and "The Pines" must have been cordial enough, to judge from letters written by Watts-Dunton to Mosher.[22]

Swinburne made a few small corrections in his copy of Mosher's edition, and sent it to press for publication with Chatto and Windus, his regular publishers since the 1870s. The proofs,

[20] Shepherd, *The Bibliography of Swinburne* (London, 1884); Wise, *A Bibliographical List of . . . Swinburne* (London, 1897).

[21] This copy of *The Tatler,* containing the complete issues from August 25 to December 29, 1877, was offered for sale by Robert H. Dodd in his catalogue, *Algernon Charles Swinburne: First Editions and an Autograph Manuscript,* February 1915, No. 16 (New York), pp. 9–10.

[22] Harvard College Library, The Mosher Papers, Nos. 1590 (Nov. 13, 1903) and 1591 (Oct. 24, 1912). On Mosher see Norman H. Strouse, *The Passionate Pirate* (North Hills, Pa., 1964); and *A Checklist of the Publications of Thomas Bird Mosher of Portland Maine MDCCCXCI MDCCCCXXIII,* compiled and edited by Benton L. Hatch, and with a biographical essay by Ray Nash (University of Massachusetts Press, 1966). The copyright technically belonged to Watts-Dunton, to whom Swinburne had given it years before; see Jean Overton Fuller, *Swinburne: A Critical Biography* (London, 1968), p. 288.

printed by Spottiswoode and Co., are stamped with dates from May 3 to May 8, 1905. Swinburne sent a set of proofs to his sister, Isabel, whose taste must have been like that of Miss Jenkyns in *Cranford*; he wrote to her on June 21:

I am very really happy to hear that you read my little old story with interest, but rather sorry you "wish it hadn't been letters." Do you know that *all* the novels approved and admired by Dr. Johnson were cast in that form? Of course, as I said to M[ary Gordon Leith] in a letter written after I received your note, it wants more attention than a flowing narrative, and bores the reader of our days unless he cares to think while reading—a little; but I have just got a letter by return of post saying she doesn't think it at all a bad way of telling a story. But I know Walter is right in saying that the public will agree with you and the book won't sell half as well as if it had been written in the third person. M. has not seen anything of it: you are the only person whom I have sent or should think of sending the proofs to.

In going over the proofs, Swinburne made minor changes in punctuation and phrasing, and a few major changes, such as the deletion of the letter "To the Author" and of the episode of the "marquis de S***"; he added the "Dedication" to Watts-Dunton, who was responsible for the new (and inferior) title, *Love's Cross-Currents*. The book was printed in an edition of 2500 copies, and published on July 12, 1905.[23] Arrangements were made for separate editions to be published at about the same time in America by Harper & Brothers and in Germany by Bernhard Tauchnitz. The first copies sold off rapidly, and a second and third impression were brought out by Chatto and Windus before the end of the year. Swinburne on August 21 wrote to W. M. Rossetti

[23] Wise, *Bibliography*, in the "Bonchurch Edition," XX, 284; *Letters*, VI, 193.

of his wonder at the success of his "more than forty-year-old book":

> if you glance at page 215 [page 140 of this edition] I think you may be reminded of a young fellow you once knew, and not see very much difference between Algie Harewood and Redgie Swinburne. Nothing in all my literary life has ever so much astonished me as the reception of this little old book. The first (small) impression, I am told, was sold out on the day of publication: and the chorus of praise from reviewers has hardly been broken by more than one or two catcalls. Honestly, I don't understand it. Still, I think the people are real flesh and blood, and I want you to like the presentation of Lady Midhurst—who is entirely a creature of my own invention—and of Reginald Harewood, who (though nothing can possibly be more different than *his parents* and mine) is otherwise rather a coloured photograph of
>
> Yours,
> A. C. Swinburne

III

This edition is the first to reproduce the text of Swinburne's manuscript, which contains important passages that were cut out for the sake of modesty rather than art, and which is more correct than any of the later versions, since they incorporate literally hundreds of verbal and punctual errors, most of them introduced by John Thomson when he made the transcript from which the later versions derive. Furthermore, at every reprinting, new errors crept in and remained undetected. Swinburne's MS. is written with extraordinary (but usual for him) clarity and consistency, and so needs hardly any emendation for the press. The few changes I have made fall under four heads:

1. Verbal alterations. In three places it has been necessary to alter obvious slips of the pen: MS. the the *changed to* the (p. 22, l.

10); grandfather's *changed to* grandfather (p. 44, l. 26); to plays *changed to* to play (p. 91, l. 20).

2. Spelling. Swinburne's own spelling, which accords more with the *Oxford English Dictionary* than with current British (or American) practice, is reproduced as it occurs in his MS. His inconsistencies in spelling (correspondence/correspondance; grey / gray; shew / show; tho' / though) and treatment of compounds (such as: dare say / daresay; sea-side / seaside), and use of capitals (such as: Church / church), are followed, with one exception: MS. thier *changed to* their (p. 24, l. 5). Also, MS. Gitaña *is changed to* Gitana (p. 55, l. 25). I have retained hyphens in three compounds broken at the end of a line: finger-tips (p. 25, l. 25), long-breathed (p. 107, l. 26), unborn-baby (p. 146, l. 20). The only place in this text where a hyphenated compound is broken at the end of a line is on p. 161, l. 21: tooth-and-nail. On p. 162, l. 31, the form is: schooldays (but compare p. 111, l. 14). Short forms which occur in places where they are mere space-savers, as in closely written or interlined passages, are expanded: MS. Ly *changed to* Lady (p. 30, l. 15; p. 96, ll. 22, 25); MS. wd *changed to* would (p. 23, l. 18; p. 94, l. 19); MS. wh: *changed to* which (p. 120, l. 32); MS. yr *changed to* your (p. 152, l. 7). Ampersands have throughout been printed in full: & *changed to* and.

3. Punctuation. Punctuation is reproduced as it appears in Swinburne's MS.: except that I have here and there removed a redundant mark where Swinburne inserted before a comma an addition which he ended with a comma; and I have supplied one or two missing periods at the end of sentences, before a capital letter. Sometimes it is not clear whether a mark is intended to be a colon or a semicolon; and the ambiguity is compounded because Swinburne uses the marks somewhat indiscriminately. In such cases I have made the decision as best I could, but not without recognizing that another reader might have decided differently. Variations in the numbering of footnotes (in letter 16), the arrangement of headings, and other merely typographical matters, have been made consistent with the predominant forms in the MS.

4. Correction of defects. In three places bits of the paper have been torn away; lost words or parts of words are supplied with the help of the transcript: so[mehow] (p. 137, l. 5); [be]cause (p. 138, l. 2); wh[ich] (p. 164, l. 7); rig[ht] (p. 164, l. 16); [must] take (p. 165, l. 5); [in t]he (p. 165, l. 14). In five places words are illegible because they are blotted and covered over by tape which was used to strengthen the paper where it had been folded. The passages are as follows, with the bracketed parts representing words that have been supplied:

Page 161, l. 34–p. 162, l. 2: serviceable [as a sauce to it]. A cl[eric] who is also a man of this w[orld and has nothing of the crossbone type] is as perfect company as you [can get or want. But conceive]

Page 163, ll. 31–32: I should guess too that she [gave hints]

Page 164, l. 23: fit to [burn. To]

Page 164, ll. 26–31: the curtain [lap]s down over it. Lucky it never turned to the tearful st[yle as it once] threatened to [do.]
    I need not say that Redgie does not exp[ect] to love [seriou]sly again. [Not] that he says it; he has just enough sense [of humour to keep the assertion] down

Page 165, ll. 19–22: We [owe h]im something; however, we may look for time to pay it. I will [confes]s to you that if the child had been a girl I meant to have brought [you to]gether at some future day. You must forgive me: for the heir's marrying [the d]ow[ag]er (This passage is lacking from the transcript, and the bracketed parts are therefore supplied from the text of *The Tatler*.)

There are many minor variations in the texts: so many that a record of them all would be long without being proportionately useful; therefore the textual notes which follow the novel give a selection from the cancelled passages in Swinburne's MS. and from his revisions in the later versions of the text. The textual notes are followed by explanatory notes clarifying allusions and pointing out parallels both biographical and literary. Persons and works not noted and not at once recognizable (such as Blamont,

Ramel, Versac, Miss Cherbury, *Vingt-et-Un,* the *Timon*) appear to be fictional. Where I could I have given the sources of quotations.

IV

List of Texts

[A Year's Letters.] Swinburne's autograph manuscript. MS. Ashley 5073, The British Library. 92 folios written on 167 sides. Title lacking. There are watermark dates on 40 folios: 1862 (37), 1860 (2), 1866 (1).

A Year's Letters, by Mrs. Horace Manners. John Thomson's transcript of Swinburne's MS. J. A. Symington Collection, No. .S978 / v. 40, Special Collections Department, Rutgers University Library. 130 folios, including title page and dedication ("To / *My Husband"*—not included in Swinburne's MS.). Originally 154 folios, but 24 are missing. There are watermark dates on 68 folios: 1868 (20), 1867 (18), 1864 (25), 1847 (4), 1846 (1). Contains Swinburne's MS. alterations, and John Nichol's MS. suggestions for revision, and printer's notations.

A Year's Letters. By Mrs. Horace Manners. *The Tatler,* Vol. II, Nos. 1–19 (August 25–December 29, 1877). The text was set up from Thomson's transcript, but Swinburne evidently made minor changes in proofs, which have not survived. The only complete copy of *The Tatler* that I know of is in the British Library.

A Year's Letters, by Algernon Charles Swinburne (Portland, Maine: Thomas B. Mosher, 1901). An unauthorized edition, printed from the text in *The Tatler.* 450 copies on Van Gelder paper, and 50 numbered copies on Japan vellum. There are copies of both kinds in the Harvard College Library, and in the Mayfield Collection. A copy with MS. alterations by Swinburne, and printer's notations, is in the J. A. Symington Collection, Special Collections Department, Rutgers University Library.

Love's Cross-Currents: A Year's Letters. Proofs printed by Spottiswoode & Co. for Chatto and Windus, dated May 3, 4, 6, and 8, 1905, with alterations in Swinburne's hand and notations in other hands. Signature C (pp. 17–32) and leaf D1 (pp. 33–34) are missing. Printed from Swinburne's copy of the Mosher edition. J. A. Symington Collection, Special Collections Department, Rutgers University Library. (Second proofs were evidently set up from these corrected sheets, but they have not survived.)

Love's Cross-Currents: A Year's Letters, by Algernon Charles Swinburne (London: Chatto & Windus, 1905). New impressions were made the same year with the addition of the words *Second Impression* and *Third Impression* on p. [iv]. The first impression has the error *albe* for *able* on p. 244, l. 18, and in all copies I have seen except one at Yale (No. Ip/Sw63/905) the colon after *beauty* on p. 254, l. 15, has dropped out. The second and third impressions correct these errors, but drop the signing G2 on p. 83.

Love's Cross-currents: [sic] *A Year's Letters,* by Algernon Charles Swinburne (New York and London: Harper & Brothers Publishers, 1905). An American edition, with essentially the same text as the Chatto and Windus edition, except for slight variations in punctuation and hyphenation.

Love's Cross-Currents: A Year's Letters, by Algernon Charles Swinburne, Author of "Atalanta in Calydon," Etc., Copyright Edition [Collection of British Authors, vol. 3834] (Leipzig: Bernhard Tauchnitz, 1905). The text is essentially the same as that of the Chatto and Windus edition.

The Complete Works of Algernon Charles Swinburne, edited by Sir Edmund Gosse, C. B. and Thomas James Wise [The Bonchurch Edition], 20 vols. (London: William Heinemann Ltd., New York: Gabriel Wells, 1925–1927). *Love's Cross-Currents: A Year's Letters* takes up pp. 65–258 of vol. VII (1926). The text is essentially the same as that of the Chatto and Windus edition.

The Novels of A. C. Swinburne: Love's Cross-Currents, Lesbia Brandon, with an introduction by Edmund Wilson (New York: Farrar, Straus and Cudahy [1962]). Also published as a paperback, with the imprint: The Noonday Press, a division of Farrar, Straus and Cudahy [1963]. *Love's Cross-Currents: A Year's Letters* takes up pp. 39–184. The text is essentially the same as that of the Chatto and Windus edition, except for the inclusion of the letter "To the Author," the text of which was apparently taken from Thomson's transcript.

Love's Cross-Currents: A Year's Letters, by Algernon Charles Swinburne, with an afterword by Marya Zaturenska, A Signet Classic ([New York:] The New American Library [1964]). According to a note on p. 158, the text of this paperback edition is reprinted from the Harper and Brothers edition, with spelling and punctuation altered to conform with modern British usage.

Critical Discussions

There are lists of book reviews of *Love's Cross-Currents* in T. G. Ehrsam et al., *Bibliographies of Twelve Victorian Authors* (New York, 1936), and in J. O. Jordan's dissertation, cited below. The most valuable are in the *Athenæum,* [vol. 126] No. 4058 (Aug. 5, 1905), 165–166; and in *Harper's Weekly,* 49, No. 2538 (Aug. 12, 1905), 1160 (by C. H. Gaines). John Drinkwater, in *Swinburne: An Estimate* (London, 1913), 188–189, gives an elegantly expressed estimate of the novel. Georges Lafourcade's learned account is as invaluable as the rest of his richly detailed study, *La Jeunesse de Swinburne* (Paris, 1928), II, 285–300. Randolph Hughes, in his edition of *Lesbia Brandon* (London, 1952), pp. 283–318, comments provocatively on *Love's Cross-Currents*. The most appealing and engaging of the published discussions is by Edmund Wilson, "Swinburne of Capheaton and Eton," *The New Yorker*, 38, No. 33 (Oct. 6, 1962), 165–200; reprinted in slightly different form in his edition of *The Novels of A. C. Swinburne*. Two excellent dissertations contain illuminating insights: John Orr Jordan, "The Novels of Algernon C. Swinburne," Stanford University, 1968; L. E. K. Brenneisen, "Plot, Character, and Setting in the Novels of Algernon C. Swinburne," Stanford University, 1972. Both can be had from University Microfilms, Ann Arbor, Michigan.

To the Author.

To the Author.

Dear Madam—

I have read your manuscript with the due care and attention, and regret that I cannot but pass upon it a verdict anything but favourable. A long sojourn in France, it appears to me, has vitiated your principles and confused your judgment. Whatever may be the case abroad, you must know that in England marriages are usually prosperous; that among us divorces are unknown, and infidelities incomprehensible. The wives and mothers of England are exempt, through some inscrutable but infallible law of nature, from the errors to which women in other countries (if we may trust the evidence of tradition) are but too fatally liable. If I understand aright the somewhat obscure drift of your work, you represent at least one married Englishwoman who prefers to her husband another man unattached to her except by illicit ties. This may happen on the continent; in England it cannot happen. You are not perhaps aware that some years since it was proposed to establish among us a Divorce Court. In a very few months it collapsed, amid the jeers and hoots of a Christian and matrimonial people. There were no cases to be tried, the lawyers retained had no chance of success or profit. England passed through the furnace of this trial, and came out pure. Tested by the final and inevitable verdict of public opinion, the Divorce Court was found superfluous and impertinent. Look into the English papers, and you will see no reports, no trials, no debates on this subject. Marriage in England is indissoluble, is sacred, is fortunate in every instance. Only a few—happily a very few—perverse and fanciful persons still venture to imagine or to suggest that a British household can be other than the chosen home of constancy and felicity. We know, if you do not, that all husbands, all wives, and all children, born or bred or married within the boundary of the three seas, are in consequence good and happy. We do not expect foreigners to understand, to believe, or to admire. We do not aspire to the suffrage or the emulation of inferior races. We are hurt only when any one born among us so far forgets the duties entailed by that singular privilege as to speak or write of England as though its men and women were no better and nobler than the rest of the world. And this, I cannot but feel, you have here done. Let me request you to reconsider your work. It appears to me doubtful whether or not you have any sufficient sense of moral beauty. Without this you can achieve no success, you can perform no work, worthy of an earnest thinker in a Christian epoch. And our own time, you must know, will most surely in the long run tolerate nothing that falls short of this standard.

I recommend you therefore to suppress or even to destroy this book, for two reasons: it is a false picture of domestic life in England; because it suggests as possible the chance that a married lady may prefer some stranger to her husband, which is palpably and demonstrably absurd; it is also, as far as I can see, deficient in purpose and significance. Morality, I need not add, is the soul of art; and picture, poem, or story, must be judged by the lesson it conveys. If it strengthens our hold upon fact, if it heightens our love of truth, if it rekindles our ardour for the right, it is admissible as good; if not, what shall we say of it?

I remain, Madam,

Yours sincerely

xxxxxx.

A YEAR'S LETTERS

Prologue.

I.

In the spring of 1849, old Lord Cheyne, the noted philanthropist, was, it will be remembered by all those interested in social reform, still alive and energetic. Indeed he had some nine years of active life before him. Public baths, institutes, reading-rooms, schools, lecture-halls, all manner of improvements were yet to bear witness to his ardour in the cause of humanity. The equable eye of philosophy has long since observed that the appetite of doing good, unlike those baser appetites which time effaces and enjoyment allays, gains in depth and vigour with advancing years. A cheering truth, attested alike by the life and death of this excellent man. Not one of his admirable plans was ever known to miss fire. Reciprocal amelioration, he was wont to say, was the aim of every acquaintance he made—of every act of benevolence he allowed himself. Religion alone was wanting to complete a character almost painfully perfect. The mutual moral friction of benefits bestowed and blessings received had as it were rubbed off the edge of those qualities which go to make up the religious sentiment. The spiritual cuticle of this truly good man was so hardened by the incessant titillations of charity and of that complacency with which virtuous people look back on days well spent, that the nervous emotions of piety had no effect on it: no tickling of doctrine or devotion could excite his fancy or his faith. At least no clearer reason than this has yet been assigned in explanation of a fact so lamentable.

His son Edmund, the late lord, whose regretted decease is yet fresh in the memory of a large and sorrowing circle of friends, was just nineteen at the above date. Educated in the lap of philanthropy, suckled at the breasts of every virtue in turn, he was even then the worthy associate of his father in all schemes of improvement. Only, in the younger man, this inherited appetite for goodness took at times a somewhat singular and dangerous turn. Mr. Cheyne was a socialist, a democrat of the most advanced kind. The father was quite happy in the construction of a model cottage; the son was busied with plans for the equalization of society. The wrongs of women gave him many a sleepless night; their cause excited in him an interest all the more commendable when one considers that he never enjoyed their company in the least, and was in effect rather obnoxious to them than otherwise. The fact of this mutual repulsion had nothing to do with philanthropy. It was undeniable; but on the other hand, the moral-sublime of this young man's character was something incredible. Unlike his father, he was much worried by religious speculation. Certain phases of belief and disbelief he saw fit to embody in a series of sonnets which were privately printed under the title of *Aspirations, by a Wayfarer.* Very flabby sonnets they were, leaving in the mouth a taste of chaff and dust; but the genuine stamp of a sincere and single mind was visible throughout; which was a real comfort. "What," exclaimed one fervid critic whose feelings found expression in a rather obscure religious journal, to which a copy had been sent, "what are the considerations of rhyme and metre to those of matter and meaning? The aim of these poems is excellent, their purpose simple and noble. Where the metal is pure, what need of elaborate artistic carving? For our part, we prefer a badly drawn and faintly coloured picture representing an act of virtue—say a sister of charity visiting the sick—to the most gorgeous and laboured reproduction of a scene better forgotten—for instance, the monstrous diversion of a show of gladiators. The rudest sketch that awakes in us a moral sense, that rekindles within us the wavering flame of virtue, is of more price in our sight than any mere display of technical skill—than any mere description or depiction of material beauty." Which is surely most creditable to the critic.

The wife of Lord Cheyne, not unnaturally, had died in giving birth to such a meritorious portent. Malignant persons, incapable of appreciating the moral-sublime, said that she died of a plethora of conjugal virtue on the part of her husband. It is certain that less sublime samples of humanity did find the society of Lord Cheyne a grievous infliction. Reform, emancipation, manure, the right of voting, the national burden, the adulteration of food, mechanics, farming, sewerage, beet-root sugar, and the loftiest morality formed each in turn the staple of that excellent man's discourse. If an exhausted visitor sought refuge in the son's society, Mr. Cheyne would hold forth by the hour on divorce, church questions, pantheism, socialism (Christian or simple), the equilibrium of society, the duties of each class, the mission of man, the balance of ranks, education, development, the stages of faith, the meaning of the age, the relation of parties, the regeneration of the priesthood, the reformation of criminals, and the destiny of woman. Decidedly the house might have been livelier than it was.

Not that virtue wanted its reward. Lord Cheyne was in daily correspondence with some dozen of societies for the propagation and suppression of heaven knows what; Professor Swallow, Dr. Chubbins, and Mr. Jonathan Bloman were among his friends. His son enjoyed the intimacy of M. Adrien Laboissière, secretary of the committee of a minor democratic society; he had received a letter from the eminent ex-citizen Poltat beginning "Salut et fraternité!" and ending with an assurance that "la foi de l'absolu lui posait au front le bandeau funèbre et majestueux de toutes les souffrances humaines." Mlle Clémence de Massigny, the too celebrated authoress of *Rosette et Rosine, Confidences d'un Fauteuil,* and other dangerous books, had, when in the full glow of her brief political career as the typical apostolic she-socialist, written to the young son of the pale and brumous Albion, "pays

[9]

des libertés tronquées et des passions châtrées," an epistle of some twenty pages, in which she desired him at least seven times to kiss the paper where she had left a kiss for him—"baiser chaste et frémissant," she averred, "étreinte altière et douce de l'esprit dégagé des pièges hideux de la matière, témoin et sceau d'un amour idéal."

"O poète!" she exclaimed elsewhere, "versons sur cette triste humanité la rosée rafraîchissante de nos pleurs; mêlons sur nos lèvres le soupir qui console au sourire qui rayonne. Chaque larme qui tombe peut rouler dans une plaie qu'elle soulagera. Les voluptés âcres et sévères de l'attendrissement valent bien le plaisir orageux des sens allumés." All this was astonishing, but satisfactory, to the recipient, and worth at least any two of his father's letters. Chubbins, Bloman and the rest, practical men enough in their way, held in some contempt the infinite and the ideal, and were incapable of appreciating the absolute republic and the forces of the future.

The arid virtue of the two chiefs was not common to the whole family. Mr. John Cheyne, younger brother to the noted philanthropist, had lived at a great rate for years; born into the regency period, he had grasped the receding skirt of its fashions; he had made friends with his time, and sucked his orange to some purpose before he came to the rind. He married well, not before it was high time; his finances, inherited from his mother, and originally not bad for a younger son, were shaken to the last screw that kept both ends together; he was turned forty and his wife had a decent fortune: she was a Miss Banks, rather handsome, sharp and quick in a good-natured way. She brought him a daughter in 1836, and a son in 1840; then, feeling no doubt that she had done all that could be looked for from a model wife, completed her good work by dying in 1841. John Cheyne consoled himself with the reflection that she might have done worse: his own niece, the wife of a neighbour and friend, had eloped the year before, leaving a boy of two on her husband's hands. For the reasons of this we must go some way back and bring up a fresh set of characters, so as to get things decently clear at starting.

A reference to the Peerage will give, as third on the Cheyne family list of the last generation, the name of "Helena, born 1800, married in 1819 Sir Thomas Midhurst, Bart. by whom (deceased) she had one daughter, Amicia, born 1820, married in May 1837 to Captain Philip Harewood, by whom she has issue, Reginald-Edward, born April 7*th* 1838. This marriage was dissolved in 1840 by act of parliament:" and we may add, Mrs. Harewood was remarried in the same year to Frederick Stanford Esq. of Ashton Hildred, co. Bucks, to whom in 1841 she presented a daughter, named after herself at the father's desire: the same, we need scarcely say, who in 1859 married the late Lord Cheyne, just ten months after his father's lamented decease. Lady Midhurst, then already widowed, took up her daughter's cause energetically at the time of the divorce. Her first son-in-law was her favourite abhorrence; with her second she has always been on the best of terms, residing indeed now for many years past with him and his wife, an honoured inmate for the term of her natural life, and in a quiet though effectual way mistress of the whole household. It was appalling to hear her hold forth on the topic of the unhappy Captain Harewood. She had known him intimately before he married her daughter; at that time he thought fit to be delightful; after the marriage, he unmasked at once and became detestable. (Fan and foot, clapping down together, used to keep time to this keen-voiced declaration.) He had used his wife dreadfully; and to this day his treatment of the poor boy left in his hands was horrible, disgraceful for its stupidity and cruelty: such a nice fellow the child was too, not the least like him but the image of his mother and of her (Lady Midhurst), which of course was reason enough for that ruffian to ill-use his own son. There was one comfort, she had leave to write to the boy and go now and then to see him, and she took care to encourage him in his revolt against his father's style of training. In effect, as far as she could, Lady Midhurst tried to instil into her grandson her own views of his father's character; it was not difficult, seeing that father and son were utterly unlike and discordant; and by the time the boy had grown up, she would bring him and his mother together again. Old Lord Cheyne—who took decidedly the Harewood side, and used sometimes to have the boy over to Lidcombe, where he revelled about the stables all day long—once remonstrated with his sister on this course of tactics. "My dear Cheyne," she replied in quite a surprised voice, "you forget Captain Harewood's estate is entailed." He was an ex-captain; his elder brother had died before he paid court to Miss Midhurst, and when he married the captain had land to settle on. As a younger brother, Lady Midhurst had liked him extremely; as a man of marriageable income, she gave him her daughter and fell at once to hating him. Ask any male novelist whether caprice is not the soul of woman.

Capricious or not, she was (and is) a beautiful old woman to look at; something like her brother John, who had been one of the handsomest men of his day; her daughter and granddaughter, both women of singular beauty and personal grace, inherited their looks and carriage from her. Clear-skinned, with pure regular features, and abundant bright white hair, (it turned suddenly, some ten years after this date, in the sixtieth of her age) she was a study for old ladies. People liked to hear her talk; she was not unwilling to gratify them. At one time of her life, she has been known to say, her tongue got her into some trouble, and her style of sarcasm involved her in various unpleasant little differences and difficulties. All that was ever said against her she managed somehow to outlive, and at fifty and upwards was very generally popular. Except indeed with religious or philanthropic persons. These, with the native instinct of race, smelt out at once an enemy in her. At sight of her acute attentive smile and reserved eyes, a curate would become hot, incoherent, finally dumb; a lecturer nervous, and voluble to the last. For the worldling's sneer may silence religion; but philanthropy is a tough fox, and dies hard. The pietist may subside on attack into actual sermonizing, and thence into a dumb shuddering appeal against what he hears—the impotence of sincere disgust; but infinite coarse chaff will not shut up the natural lecturer; he snuffs sharply at your implied objection, and comes up to time again, gasping, verbose, and resolute.

II.

The two children of Mr. John Cheyne enjoyed somewhat less of their aunt's acquaintance and care than did her grandchildren—or even her other nephew, Lord Cheyne's politico-philanthropic son and successor. They were brought up in the quietest way possible; Clara with a governess who took her well in hand at an early age, and kept her apart from all influence but her own; Frank under the lazy kind incurious eyes of his father, who coaxed him into a little shaky Latin at his spare hours, with a dim vision before him of Eton as soon as the boy should be fit. Lord Cheyne now and then exchanged visits with his brother, but not often; and the children not unnaturally were quite incapable of appreciating the earnest single-minded philanthropy of the excellent man. Their father hardly relished it more than they did; but there was one man, or boy, whom John Cheyne held in deeper and sincerer abhorrence than he did his brother; and this was his brother's son. Mr. Cheyne called betweenwhiles at his uncle's, but was hardly received with a decent welcome. A clearer-sighted or more speculative man than John Cheyne would have smelt a nascent inclination on his nephew's part towards his daughter. There was a sort of weakly weary gentleness of manner in the young philanthropist which the girl soon began to appreciate. Clara shewed early enough a certain acuteness, and a relish of older company which gave promise of some practical ability. At thirteen she had some good ideas of management, and was a match for her father in most things. But she could not make him tolerate his nephew; she could only turn his antipathy to profit by letting it throw forward into relief her own childish friendliness. There was the composition of a good intriguer in the girl from the first: and she had a desirable power of making all that could be made out of every chance of enjoyment. She was never one to let the present slip. Few children have such a keen sense as she always had, how infinitely preferable is the smallest skinny limping half-moulted sparrow in the hand to the fattest ortolan in the bush. She was handsome too, darker than her father's family; her brother had more of the Cheyne points about him. Frank was not a bad sort of boy, quiet, idle, somewhat excitable and changeable, with a good deal of loose floating affection in him, and a fund of respect for his sister. Lady Midhurst, after one of her visits (exploring cruises in search of character she called them) set him down in a decisive way as "flat, *fade,* wanting in spice and salt, the sort of boy always to do decently well in any circumstances, to get creditably through any work he might have to do; a fellow who would never tumble because he never jumped; well enough disposed no doubt, and not a milksop exactly; certain to get on comfortably with most people, if there were not more of his father latent in the boy than she saw yet; whereas if he really had inherited anything of her brother John's headstrong irresolute nature, she was sure he had no strong qualities to counterbalance or modify it." Lady Midhurst rather piqued herself on this exhaustive elaborate style of summary; and had indeed a good share of insight and analytic ability. Her character of Frank was mainly unfair; but that quality of "always doing well enough under any circumstances" the boy really had in some degree; a rather valuable quality too. His aunt would have admitted the value of it at once; but he was "not her sort (she would have added), she liked people who made their own scrapes for themselves before they fell into them, and then got out without being fished for. Frank would get into trouble sometimes no doubt, but he would just *slip in.* Now it was always better to fall than to slip. You got less dirty, and were less time about it; besides, an honest tumble was less likely to give you a bad sprain." This philosophic lady had a deep belief in the "discipline of circumstances," and was

[14]

disposed to be somewhat more than lenient towards any one passing (not unsoiled) through his time of probation and training. Personally at this time Frank was a fair rather short boy, with light hair, grey eyes, and usually peaceable and amiable in his behaviour; his sister tall, brown, thin, with clear features, and something of an abrupt decisive air about her. They had few friends and saw little company; Captain Harewood, who in former days had been rather an intimate of John Cheyne's, hardly ever now rode over to see his ex-friend; not that he had any quarrel with the uncle of his divorced wife, but he scarcely ever now stirred out or sought any company beyond a few professional men of his own stamp and a clergyman or two, having lately taken up with a rather acrid and dolorous kind of religion. Lady Midhurst, one regrets to say, asserted that her enemy made a mere pretence of austerity in principle, and spent his time under cover of seclusion in the voluptuous pastime of torturing his unlucky boy and all his miserable subordinates; "the man was always one of those horrid people who cannot live without giving pain; she remembered he was famous for cruelty in his profession, and certainly he had always been the most naturally cruel and spiteful man she ever knew; she had not an atom of doubt he really had some nervous physical pleasure in the idea of others' sufferings; that was the only way to explain the whole course of his life and conduct." Once launched on the philosophy of this subject Lady Midhurst went on to quote instances of a like taste which we forbear from giving. As to the unfortunate Captain Harewood nothing could be falser than such an imputation; he was merely a grave dry shy soured man, severe and sincere in his sorrowful reserve and distaste for company. Perhaps he did enjoy his own severity and moroseness and had some occult pleasure in the sense that his son was being trained up sharply and warily; but did not a boy with such blood in his veins need it?

Thus there was one source of company cut off for the first years of their life from the young Cheynes. The only companion they were usually sure of was not much to count on in the way of amusement: being a large heavy solitary boy of sixteen or more, a son of their neighbour on the left, Mr. Radworth of Blocksham. These Radworths were allies of old Lord Cheyne's, who had a great belief in the youth's genius and promise; he had developed when quite young a singular taste and aptitude for science, abstract and mechanical; had carried on this study at school in the teeth of his tutors and in defiance of his schoolfellows, keeping well aloof from all other learning, and taking little rest or relaxation. His knowledge and working power were wonderful; but he was a slow, unlovely, weighty, dumb grim sort of fellow, and had already overtasked his brain and nerves, besides ruining his eyes. He never went anywhere but to the Cheynes', and there used to pay a dull puzzled homage to the girl, who set very light by him. There was always a strong flavour of the pedant and the *philistin* about Ernest Radworth, which his juniors were of course quick enough to appreciate.

Mr. John Cheyne, though on very fair terms with his sister, did not visit the Stanfords; he had never seen his niece since the time of the divorce; Lady Midhurst was the only member of the household at Ashton Hildred who ever came across to his place. His two children hardly knew the name of their small second cousin, Amicia Stanford; she was a year younger than Frank Cheyne, and the petted pupil of her grandmother. Mrs. Stanford, a gentle handsome woman, lazy and rather shy in her manner, gave the child up wholly to the elder lady's care, and spent her days chiefly in a soft sleepy kind of housekeeping. A moral observer would have deplored the evident quiet happiness of her life. She never thought at all about her first husband, or the three years of her life (1837–1840) which Lady Midhurst used to call her pre-Stanford period; except on those occasions when her mother broke out with some fierce reference to Captain Harewood or some angry expression of fondness for his son. Then Mrs. Stanford would cry a little, in a dispassionate graceful manner; no doubt she felt at times some bitter tender desire and regret towards the first of her children, gave way betweenwhiles to some little unprofitable memory of him; small sorrows that had not heart enough in them to last long. At one time perhaps she had wept away all the tears she had in her; one may doubt if there had ever been a great sum of them for grief to draw upon; she was of a delicate impressible make, but not fashioned so as to suffer sharply for long together; if there came any sorrow in her way she dropped down (so to speak) at the feet of it and bathed them in tears till it took pity on her tender beauty and passed by on the other side without doing her much harm. She was quite unheroic and rather unmaternal; but pleasantly and happily put together, kind, amiable, and very beautiful: and as fond as she could ever be, not only of herself, but also of her husband, her mother and her daughter. The husband was just a good sort of man, and always deep in love of his wife and admiration of her mother; never conspicuous for any event in his life but that elopement; and how matters even then had come to a crisis between two such lovers as they were, probably only one person on earth could have told; and this third person certainly was not the bereaved captain. The daughter was from her birth of that rare and singular beauty which never changes for the worse in growing older. She was one of the few girls who have no ugly time. In this spring of 1849 she was the most perfect child of eight that can be imagined. There was a strange grave beauty and faultless grace about her, more noticeable than the more usual points of childish prettiness; pureness of feature, ample brilliant hair, perfect little lips rounded and serious in shape, and wonderful unripe beauty of cheek and throat. Her grandmother, who was fond of using French phrases when excited or especially affectionate (derived from recollections of her own French mother and early friends among French relatives; she had a way of saying Hein? and glancing up or sideways with an eye at once bird-like and feline), asserted that Amy was faite à peindre—faite à croquer—faite à manger de baisers. The old life-worn philosophic lady seemed absolutely to riot and revel in her fondness for the child. There was always a certain amiably cynical side to her affections, which shewed itself by and by in the girl's training; but the delight and love aroused in her at the sight of her small pupil were as true and tender as such emotions could be in such a woman. Lady Midhurst was really very much fonder of her two grandchildren than of any one else alive. Redgie was just her sort of boy, she said, and Amy just her sort of girl. It would have been delicious to bring them up together; (education, superintendance, training of character, guidance of habit in young people, were passions with the excellent lady;) and if the boy's father would just be good enough to come to some timely end! She had been godmother to both children, and both were as fond of her as possible. Enfin! she said hopelessly.

III.

They were to have enough to do with each other in afterlife, all these scattered handfuls of cousins; but the mixing process only began on a late spring day of 1849, at the country-house which Mr. John Cheyne had inherited from his wife. This was a little old house beautifully set in among orchards and meadows, with abundance of roses now all round it, under the heavy leaves of a spring that June was fast gaining upon. A wide soft river divided the marsh-meadows in front of it, full of yellow flag-flowers and moist fen-blossom. Behind there slanted upwards a small broken range of hills, the bare green windy lawns of them dry and fresh under foot, thick all the way with cowslips at the right time. It was a splendid place for children; better perhaps than Ashton Hildred with its huge old brick-walled gardens, and wonderful fruit-trees blackened and dotted with lumps or patches of fabulous overgrown moss, and wild pleasure-grounds stifled with beautiful rank grass: better decidedly than Lord Cheyne's big brilliant Lidcombe, in spite of royal shooting-grounds and the admirable slopes of high bright hill-country behind it, and green sweet miles of park and embayed lake, beyond praise for riding or boating; better incomparably than Captain Harewood's place, muffled in woods, with a grim sad beauty of its own, but seemingly kneedeep in sere leaves all the year round, wet and weedy and dark and deep down, kept hold of somehow by autumn in the midst of spring, (only the upper half of it clear out of the clutch of winter even in the hottest height of August weather); with a bitter flavour of frost and rain in it all through summer. It was wonderful, Lady Midhurst said, how any child could live there without going mad or moping. She was thankful the boy went to school so young, though no doubt his father had picked out the very hardest sort of school that he decently could select. Anything was better than that horrid wet hole of a place, up to the nose and eyes in black damp woods and with thick moist copses of alder and birch trees growing against the very windows; and such a set of people inside of it! She used to call there about three times a year, during the boy's holidays; get him apart from his father and tutor, and give him presents, and advice, and pity, and encouragement of all sorts; mixed with histories of his mother and half-sister; the whole spiced not sparingly with bitter allusions to his father, to which one may fear there was some response on the boy's part.

It was after one of these visits that Captain Harewood brought his son over to his old friend's. Perhaps he thought at length that the boy might as well see some one about his own age in holiday time. Reginald was growing visibly mutinous and hard to keep down by preachings and punishments; had begun evidently to wince and kick under the domestic rod. His father, and the clerical tutor who came over daily to look after the boy's holiday tasks, could hardly keep him under by frequent flogging and much serious sorrowful lecturing. He was not a specially fast boy, only about as restless and insubordinate as most fellows at his age; but this was far more than his father was prepared to stand. Let him see some one else outside home than Lady Midhurst; it could do no harm, and the boy was always vicious, and jibbed frightfully, for some days after his grandmother's visit. So before the holidays were out the captain trotted him over to make friends with Mr. Cheyne's son. The visit was a matter of keen

[19]

and rather frightened interest to Frank; Clara, on hearing the boy was her junior, made light of it, and was out of the way when Captain Harewood came in with his son. The two boys eyed each other curiously under close brows, and with lips expressive of a grave doubt on either side. The visitor was a splendid-looking fellow, lithe and lightly built, but of a good compact make, with a sunburnt oval face and hair like unspun yellow silk in colour, but one mass of short rough curls; eyebrows, eyes and eyelashes all black, shewing quaintly enough against his golden hair and bright pale skin. His mouth, with a rather full red underlip for a child, had a look of such impudent wilful beauty as to suggest at once the frequent call for birch in such a boy's education. His eyes too had a defiant laugh latent under the lazy light in them. Rather well got up for the rest, and delicately costumed, tho' with a distinct school stamp on him; but by no means after the muscle-manful type.

This boy had a short whip in one hand which was of great and visible comfort to him. To switch his leg in a reflective measured way was at once an action impressive in itself, and likely to meet and obviate any conversational necessity that might turn up. No smaller boy could accost him lightly while in that attitude.

At last, with a gracious gravity, seeing both elders deep in low-voiced talk, he vouchsafed five valuable words; I say. What's your name?—Frank gave his name in with meekness, having a just sense of his relative insignificance. He was very honest and easy to dazzle. Mine's Reginald—Reginald Edward Harewood. It doesn't sound at all well (this with a sententious suppressed flourish in the voice, as of one who blandly deprecates a provoked contradiction); no; not at all; because there's such a lot of d's in it. Yours is a much better name. How old are you?

The abject Frank apologetically suggested, Nine.

You just look it, said Reginald Harewood, with an awful calm, indicative of a well-grounded contempt for that time of life, restrained for the present by an exquisite sense of social courtesy.

I'm eleven. Rising twelve. Eleven last month. Suppose we go out?

IV.

Once out in the garden, Reginald became more wonderful than ever. Any one not two years younger and half a head shorter must have doubled up with laughter before he had gone three steps. Our friend's patronage of the sunlight, his tolerance of the roses, his gentle thoughtful condescension towards the face of things in general, were too sublime for words.

When they came to the parapet of an old broad terrace, Reginald, still in a dignified way, got astride it; not without a curious grimace and some seeming difficulty in adjusting his small person: tapped his teeth with his whip-handle, and gave Frank for a whole minute the full benefit of his eyes. Frank stood twisting a rose-branch and looked meek.

The result of Reginald's scrutiny was this question, delivered with much solemn effect.

I say. Were you ever swished?

Swished? said Frank, with a rapid heat in his cheeks.

Swished, said Reginald in his decisive voice. Birched.

Do you mean, flogged? Frank asked this very diffidently, as if the query singed his lips.

Well, flogged, if you like that better, said Reginald, conscious of a neat point. Flogged. But I mean a real right-down swishing, you know. If a fellow says, flogged, it may be a whip don't you see, or a strap. That's caddish. But you can call it flogging if you like. Only not at school, mind. It's all very well before me.

Reverting from these verbal subtleties to the main point, Reginald put the grand query again, in a modified shape, but in a tone of courteous resolution, not to be evaded by any boy.

Does your father often flog you?

I never was flogged in my life, said Frank, sensible of his deep degradation.

Reginald, as a boy of the world, could stand a great deal without surprise; experience of men and things had inured him to much that was curious and out of the usual way. But at the shock of this monstrous and incredible assertion, he was thrown right off his balance. He got off the parapet, and leant his shoulders against it, and gazed upon the boy to whom birch was a dim dubious myth, a jocose threat after dinner, with eyebrows wonderfully high up and distended eyelids. Then he said; Good—God! softly and dividing the syllables, with hushed breath.

Goaded to insanity by the big boy's astonishment, agonized by his silence, Frank tenderly put a timid foot in it.

Were you? he asked, with much awe.

Then, with straightened shoulders and raised chin, Reginald Harewood took up his parable. Some of his expressions must be forgiven to youthful excitement, and for the sake of accuracy; boys when voluble on a tender point are awfully accurate in their choice of words. Reginald was very voluble by nature, and easy to excite on this painfully personal matter.

Ah! Yes. I should think so. My good fellow, you ought to have seen me yesterday. I was swished twice in the morning. Can't you see in a man's eyes? My father is—the—most—awful—Turk. He likes to swish me—he does really. What you'll do when you go to school—(here a pause)—God knows. (This in a pensive and devout manner, touched with pity.) You'll sing out—by Jove! won't you sing out the first time you catch it? I used to. I do sometimes now. For it hurts most awfully. But I can stand a good lot of it. There were bits cut right out of me yesterday on one side. Here. And one twig stuck in the cut and I couldn't get it out for half an hour. My father can always draw blood the third or fourth cut. It's ever so much worse than a whole swarm of mad bees stinging you at once. Makes a fellow tingle to the bone. At school, if you kick, or if you wince even, or if you make the least bit of row, you get six cuts over. I always did. When I was your age. The big fellows used to call me all manner of chaffy names: Pepperbottom, that was out of a book; I know the book; I'll bet you don't;

[22]

and the Wagtail; because I used to wriggle about on the block: between each cut; I know I did. They call me Wag now, and Pepper, for short. Not the young ones, of course. I should lick them. I say, I wish you were going to school. I'd look after you. You'd be letting fellows get you into the most awful rows. Ah! wouldn't you? When I was your age I used to get swished twice a day regular. The masters spite me. I know one of them does, because he told one of the big fellows he did. At least he said I was a curse to the whole school, and I was ruining all the young ones. He did really, on my word. I was the fellow's fag that he said it to, and he called me up that night and licked me with a whip. With a whip like this. He was a most awful bully. I don't think I'll tell you what he did once to a boy. You wouldn't sleep well to-night.

Oh, do; said Frank, quivering. The terrific interest of Reginald's confidences suspended his heart at his lips: he beheld the Complete Schoolboy with a breathless reverence; as for pity, he would as soon have ventured to pity a crowned head.

No, said the boy of the world, shaking considerate curls; I won't tell a little fellow. I think it's a shame to go and put them in a funk. Some fellows are always trying it on, for a spree. I never do. No, my good fellow, you'd better not ask me. You had really.

Reginald sucked his whip-handle with a relish, and eyed the universe in a conscious way.

Do, please; pleaded the younger: I don't mind. I've heard of—that is I've read all kind of awful things. I don't care about them the least bit.

Well, young one, said Reginald, don't blame me then, that's all, if you have bad dreams. There was one fellow ran away from school when he heard of it. On my word. Well. You see there was one of this big fellow's fags had been swished. Three dozen cuts. The twigs were all used up; some were broken right off, and the birch was quite green and fresh, and oh, no end of birch-buds on; but you see you can't understand. Of course the boy was all over jolly great weals and cuts, and as raw as they could be. Couldn't have sat down to save his life. Looked as if you'd been peppering him with powder and shot. Worse. Had to get a fellow to help and pick the bits of birch out of his flesh. Well, his master made him strip stark naked, and made two other fags about his own height take a lot of salt in their hands and rub it into the cuts. There. Rubbed him all over with salt, up and down, wherever the birch had touched him. I never felt such awful pain in my life. It made the flesh smart like mad. I'm not soft usually, but then I did howl! I roared till they heard me everywhere. But it didn't do me any harm. Only it hurt so, you can't conceive. And the other fags told and he got awfully licked by all the other big fellows; he couldn't fight in the least, and they pitched into him till he cut. Then he was brought back by his father, and got such a jolly good swishing! Six dozen cuts he got. Really and truly.

Reginald recited this pleasing episode with a dreadful unction. No description can express the full fleshy sound of certain words in his mouth; he talked of *cuts* with quite a lickerish accent, and gave the technical word *swish* with a twang in which the hissing sound of a falling birch, or the clear hard ringing noise of a tough stroke on the bare flesh, became sharply audible. His eyes glittered and his lips caressed the tingling syllables. The boy was immeasurably proud of his floggings, and relished the subject of flagellation as few men relish rare wine. As for shame, he had never for a second thought of it. A flogging was an affair of honour to him; if he came off without tears, although with loss of blood, he regarded the master with chivalrous pity, as a brave enemy worsted. A real tormentor always revelled in the punishment of Reginald; those who plied the birch with true loving delight in the use of it enjoyed the whipping such a boy intensely. Orbilius would have feasted on his flesh—dined off him.

He looked Frank between the eyes as he finished, and gave a great shrug.

I said you'd better not. You look blue and green. Upon my honour you do. It's your fault, my good fellow. I'm very sorry. I know some fellows can't stand things. I knew you couldn't. By the look of your eyes. I could have taken my oath of it. It isn't in you. It's not your fault. I dare say you've no end of pluck, but you're nervous, don't you see? I don't mean you funk exactly. Things disagree with you. That's it.

Here Reginald strangled a discourteous and compromising chuckle and gave himself a cut with his whip that made his junior wink.

Ah, now, you see. That makes you wince. Now, look here. You just take hold of that whip and give me a cut as hard as you possibly can. You just do that. I should like it. Do, there's a good fellow. I want to see if you could hurt me. Hit hard. Mind. Now then:—and he presented a bending broadside to the shot.

The trodden worm turned and stung. Driven mad by patronage, and all the more savage because of his deep admiration, Frank could not let the chance slip. He took sharp aim, set his teeth, and swinging all his body round with the force of the blow as he dealt it, brought down the whip on the tightest part he could pick out, with a vicious vigour and stinging skill.

He had a moment's sip of pure honey: Reginald jumped a foot high, and yelled.

But in another minute, before Frank had got his breath again, the boy turned round, rubbing hard with one hand, patted him, and delivered a Well done! more stinging than a dozen cuts. Frank succumbed.

I say, just let me feel your muscle, said Reginald, passing scientific finger-tips up the arm of his companion. Ah, very good muscle you've got; you ought just to keep it up, you see, and you'll do splendidly. Bend your arm up; so. I'll tell you what now, you ought to make no end of a good hitter in time. But you wouldn't have hurt me a bit if I hadn't come to such grief yesterday. Then you see riding over here one got rubbed. Riding doesn't usually make me lose leather, but to-day, you know—that is you don't know. But you will. —Reginald gave a pathetic nod indicative of untold horrors.

Frank had begun a meek excuse, which was cut short with imperious grace.

My dear fellow, don't bother yourself, I don't mind. You'll

have to learn how to stand a cut before you leave home, or the first time you're sent up, by God, how you will squeak! There was a fellow like you last half (Audley his name was) who had never been flogged till he came to school; he was a nice sort of fellow enough, but when they told him to look sharp and kneel down—look here, he went in this way. —And Reginald proceeded to enact the whole scene, making an inoffensive laurel-bush represent the flagellated novice, whose yells and contortions he rendered with fearful effect, plying his whip vigorously betweenwhiles till a rain of gashed leaves inundated the gravel, and giving at the same time vocal imitations of the swish of the absent birch-twigs and the voice of the officiating master as it fulminated words of objurgation and jocose contumely between each cut. The vivid portraiture of the awful thing, and Redgie's subsequent description (too graphic and terrible in its naked realism to be reproduced) of the appearance and demeanour of the culprit when his whipping was over, of the condition of his attire and his person, and of his usage at the hands of indignant schoolboys whose sense of propriety his base behaviour under punishment had outraged in its tenderest part—all this absolutely stung the youthful hearer with bitter pleasure and the excitement of a dreadful delight—made his blood shiver deliciously and his nerves tingle with a tremulous sympathy. It had roused in him now, besides admiration, a sort of sensual terror which was not so far from desire. He was grateful for this experience and felt older than five minutes since.

Reginald too, remarking and relishing the impression made, felt kindly towards his junior and promised by implication a continuance of his patronage. In this benign frame of mind he proposed to shew Frank his horse; and having got him to the stables desired him in an impressive way to "look at the hocks." Frank immediately began to examine the nose; but as Redgie, though he could really ride well enough, knew about as much of the proper stable terms as Frank did and had the vaguest idea of the component parts of a horse, he was quite satisfied. Thence

they went in to luncheon, when Redgie examined his friend's sister with the acute eyes of a boy of the world, and evidently approved of her—became indeed quite subdued, "lowly and serviceable," on finding that thirteen took a high tone with eleven, and was not prepared to permit advances on an equal footing. Frank meantime was scrutinizing under timid eyelids the awful Captain Harewood, in whose hand the eye of his fancy saw, instead of knife and fork, a lifted birch, the twigs worn and frayed, and spotted with filial blood.

Redgie's father was thirty-eight that year, nine years older than his ex-wife, but looking much more. Mrs. Stanford had a fresh equable beauty which might have suited a woman ten years younger. The captain was a handsome tall man, square in build, with a hard forehead; the black eyes and eyebrows he had bequeathed to his son, but softened; his own eyes were metallic and the brows heavy, shaggy even. He had a hard mouth with large locked lips; a tight chin, a full smooth moustache, and a wide cheek, already furrowed and sad-looking. Something of a despot's justice in the look of him, and something of bitter doubt and regret. His host, a man twelve or fifteen years older, had worn much better than he had.

When the boys were off again by themselves, Redgie was pleased to express his sense of the merits of Frank's sister: a tribute gratefully accepted. Clara was stunning for a girl, her brother added; but was cautious of overpraising her.

I've got a sister, Reginald stated; I believe she's a clipper but I don't know. Oh, I say, isn't my grandmother an aunt of yours or something?

Aunt Helena? said her nephew, who held her in a certain not unfriendly awe.

That's her, said Redgie, using a grammatical construction which, occurring in a Latin theme, would have brought down birch on his bare skin to a certainty. Isn't she a brick? I think she's the greatest I know. That's about what she is.

Frank admitted she was kind.

[27]

Kind? I should think she was too. She's a trump. But do you know she hates my governor like mad. They hardly speak when she comes to our crib. Last time she came she gave me a fiver—she did really. (Redgie, at that age, wanted usually some time to get up his slang in, but when it once began he was great at it, considering he had never got into a very slang set.) Well, she says my sister is no end of a good one to look at by this time; but I think yours must be the jolliest. I've known lots of girls (the implied reticence of accent was, as Lady Midhurst would have said, *impayable*) but I never saw such a stunner as she is. She makes a fellow feel quite shut up and spooney.

This amorous confidence was brought up short by the sudden advent of the two fathers. Meeting the eye of his, Redgie felt his fate, and tingled with the anticipated smart of it. All his last speech had too clearly dropped word by word into the paternal ear; and the wretched boy's face reddened with biting blushes to the very chin and eyelids and hair. When some twenty minutes later they parted at the hall-door, Redgie gave his friend a pitiful private wink and sadly comic shrug, so suggestive of (his impending doom and) the inevitable ceremony to be gone through when he reached home again, that Frank, having seen him ride off quite silently a little behind his father, turned back into the house with his own flesh quivering and a fearful vague vision before his eyes of Reginald, some hours later, twisting his bared limbs under the torture.

He was eager to gather the household verdicts on his friend; but Reginald had scarcely made much of a success in other quarters. Clara thought him silly and young of his age (a verdict which would have finished him at once if he had known of it), but admitted he was a handsome boy, much prettier and pleasanter to have near one than Ernest Radworth. Mr. Cheyne was sorry for the boy, but could hardly put up with such a sample of the new race; Redgie's conceit and gracious impudence (though it was not really a case of bad tone, he allowed) had evidently been too much

[28]

for him. The Captain too had expressed uneasiness about his boy, and a sense of vexatious outlooks ahead.

After all, there grew up no great intimacy out of this first visit; a mere grotesque childish interlude, which seemingly had but just result enough to establish a certain tie at school afterwards between young Cheyne and his second cousin—a tie considerably broken in upon by various squabbles, and strained often almost to snapping; but for all that the visit had left its mark on both sides, and had its consequences.

V.

We have taken a flying view of these domestic affairs and the people involved in them, as they stood twelve years or so before the date of the ensuing correspondence. Something may now be understood of the characters and positions of these people; enough no doubt to make the letters comprehensible without interpolated notes or commentaries. Much incident is not here to be looked for; what story there is to tell ought at least to be given with clearness and coherence. There remains only, by way of preface, to sum up the changes that fell out between 1849 and 1861.

At the latter date, two deaths and two marriages had taken place; old Lord Cheyne, much bewept by the earnest and virtuous men of all classes, had died, laborious to the last in the great cause of human amelioration; and his son, a good deal sobered by lapse of time and friction of accident, had married (in May 1859; within a year of his accession, as aforesaid) his cousin Mrs. Stanford's daughter; she was married on her eighteenth birthday, and there was no great ado made about it. John Cheyne had died a year before his brother; having lived long enough to see his daughter well married, in 1855, to Mr. Ernest Radworth, whose fame as a man of science had gone on increasing ever since he came into his property in 1853, at the age of twenty. His researches in osteology were of especial value and interest; he was in all ways a man of great provincial mark.

There is not much else to say; unless it may be worth adding, that Francis Cheyne was at college by this time, with an eye to the bar in years to come; his father's property had been much cut into by the share assigned to his sister, and there was just a fair competence left him to start upon. When not at Oxford, he lived usually either at Lidcombe or Blocksham, seldom by himself at home; but had for some little time back shewn a distinct preference of his cousin's house to his brother-in-law's: Lord Cheyne and he being always on the pleasantest terms. With this cousin, though ten years older than himself, he got on now much better than with his old companion Reginald Harewood, whose Oxford career had just ended in the passing over his hapless head of the untimely plough; and whose friends, all but Lady Midhurst, had pretty well washed their hands of him.

～

1.

Lady Midhurst to Mrs. Radworth.

Ashton Hildred, Jan. 12*th* '61

My dear Niece—I write to beg a favour of you, and you are decidedly the one woman alive I could ask it of. There is no question of me in the matter, I assure you; I know how little you owe to a foolish old aunt, and would *on no account* tax your forbearance so far as to assume the very least air of dictation. You will hardly remember what good friends we used to be when you were *a very small member of society indeed*. If I tried then to *coax* you into making it up with your brother after some baby dispute, I recollect I always broke down in a lamentable way. The one chance at that time was to put the thing before you on rational grounds: I am trying to act on that experience now.

This is rather a stupid *grand* sort of beginning, when all I really have to say is that I want to see the whole family on comfortable terms again, and especially to make you and Amicia friends. For you know it is hopeless to persuade an old woman who is not quite in her dotage that there has not been a certain coldness—say tiédeur—of late in the relations between you and those Lidcombe people. Since my poor brother's death no doubt the place has not had those attractions for Mr. Radworth which it had when there was always some scientific or philanthropic gathering there; indeed I suppose your house has pretty well supplanted Lidcombe as the rallying-point of provincial science for miles. By all I hear you are becoming quite eminent in that line, and it must be delicious for you personally to see how thoroughly your husband begins to be appreciated. I quite envy you the society you must see and the pleasure you must take in seeing and sharing Mr. Radworth's enjoyment of it. (I trust his

[31]

sight is improving steadily.) But for all this you should not quite cast off less fortunate people who have not the same tastes and pursuits. You and Cheyne were once so comfortable and intimate that *I am certain* he must frequently regret this change: and Amicia, as you know, sets far more store by you than any other friend she could have about her. Do be prevailed upon to take pity on the poor child: her husband is a delightful one, and most eager to amuse and gratify, but *I know* she wants a companion. At her age, my dear, I could not have lived without one; and at yours, if you were not such a philosopher, you ought to be as unable as I was. Men have their uses and their merit, I allow, but you cannot *live* on them. My friend by the by was not a good instance to cite, for she played me a fearful trick once; Lady Wells her name was; I had to give her up in the long run, but she was charming at one time, wonderfully bright in her ways, at once quick and soft as it were; just my idea of Madame de Léry in *Un Caprice.* She was idolized by all sorts of people, authors particularly, for she used to hunt them down with a splendid skill and make great play with them when caught; but the things the woman used to say! and then the people about her went off and set them all down in their books. The men actually took her stories as samples of what went on daily in a certain circle, and wrote them down, altering the names, as if they had been gospel. She told me some before they got into print: there was nobody she would not mix up in them. One had to break with her at last, in a peaceable way. If you ever see an old novel called (I think) *Vingt-et-Un* or some such name—I know there are *cards* in it—you will find a picture there of your aunt painted by the author (a Mr. Caddell) after a design by Lady Wells. I am the Lady Manhurst of that nice book. I cheat at cards. I break the heart of a rising poet (that is, I never would let Sir Thomas invite Mr. Caddell). I make two brothers fight a duel, and one is killed through my direct agency. I run away with a Lord Avery. I am not certain that my husband dies a natural death: I rather think indeed that I poison him in the last chapter but one. Finally I become a

Catholic; Lord Avery recognizes me in the conventual garb, the day after my noviciate is out, and immediately takes leave of his senses. I hope I died penitent, but I really forget about that. You see what sort of things one could make people believe in those days: I suppose there is no fear of a *liaison dangereuse* of that sort between you and poor little Amicia. She has not much of the Lady Wells type in her.

I have a graver reason, as you probably imagine by this time, for wishing you to see a little of Amicia just now. It is rather difficult to write about, but I am sure you will see things better for yourself than I could make you if I were to scribble for ever in this cautious roundabout way: and I can trust so thoroughly in your good feeling and good sense and acuteness, that I know you will do what is right and useful and honourable. It is a great thing to know of anybody who has a *head* that can be relied upon. Good hearts and good feelings are easy to pick up, but a good clear sensible head is a godsend. Nothing else could ever get us through this little family business in reasonable quiet.

I fear you must have heard of some absurd running rumours about your brother's last stay at Lidcombe. People who always see what never exists are beginning to talk of his *devotion* to poor dear Amicia. Now I of course know, and you of course know, that there never *could* be anything serious on foot in such a quarter; the boy is hardly of age, and might be at school as far as that goes. Besides, Cheyne and Amicia are perfectly devoted to each other, as we all see. My only fear would be for poor Frank himself. If he did get any folly of a certain kind into his head it might cause infinite personal trouble, and give serious pain to more people than one. I have seen more than once how much real harm may come of such things. I wonder if you ever heard your poor father speak of Mrs. Askew—Walter Askew's wife, who was a great beauty in our time? Both my brothers used to rave about her; she had features of that pure long type you get in pictures, and eyes that were certainly mieux fendus than any I ever saw, dim deep grey, half-lighted under the heaviest eyelids, with a sleepy sparkle in them; faulty in her carriage, very; you had to look at her sitting to understand the effect she used to make. Her husband was very fond of her, and a cleverish sort of man, but too light and lazy to do all he should have done. Well, a Mr. Chetwood, the son of a very old friend of mine (they used to live here), became infatuated about her. Spent days and days in pursuit of her; made himself a perfect jest. Everywhere she went there was this wretched man hanging on at her heels; they were not much to hang on to, by the by, for she had horrid feet. To this day I believe he never got anything by it; if the woman ever cared for anybody in her life it was your father: but Mr. Askew had to take notice of it at last; the other got into a passion and insulted him (I am afraid they were both over-excited—it was after one of my husband's huge dinners and they came up in a most dreadful state of rage, and trying to behave well, with their faces actually trembling all over and the most fearful eyes) and there was a duel and the husband was killed, and Chetwood had to fly the country, people made it out such a bad case, and he was ruined—died abroad within the year: he had spent all his money before this last business. The woman afterwards married Dean Bainbridge, the famous Waterworth preacher you know, who used to be such a friend of my friend Captain Harewood's for the last year or two of his life; he had buried his third wife by that time; Mrs. A. was the second. He was a detestable man, and had a voice exactly like a cat with a bad cold in the head.

Now if anything of this sort were to happen to Francis (not that I am afraid of my two nephews' cutting each other's throats—but so much may happen short of that!) it is just the kind of thing he might never get well over. He and Amy are about the same age I think, or he may be a year older. In a case like this, of amicable intimacy between two persons, one married, there is necessarily a certain floating amount of ridicule implied, even where there is nothing worse; and the whole of this ridicule must fall in the long run upon the elder person of the two. I am not sure of course that there is any ground for fear just now; but to avoid the least chance of scandal, still more of ridicule, it is always worth while being at *any* pains. Nobody knows *how* well worth while it is till they are turned of thirty. Now you must see, supposing there is anything in this unfortunate report, that I cannot possibly be of the least use. Imagine me writing to that poor child to say she must not see so much of her cousin, or to Frank imploring him to spare the domestic peace of Lidcombe! It would be too absurd for me to seem as if I saw or heard anything of the matter. A screeching cackling grandmother running round the yard with all her frowsy old feathers ruffled at the sight of such a miserable red rag as that would be a thing to laugh at for a year: and I have no intention of helping people to a laugh at my white hairs (they are quite white now).

Or would you have me write to Cheyne? La bonne farce! as Redgie Harewood says since he has been in Paris. Conceive the delicate impressive way one would have to begin the letter in, so as not to arouse the dormant serpents in a husband's heart. Think of the soft suggestive Iago style one would have to adopt, so as to intimate the awfullest possibilities without any hard flat assertion. Poor good Edmund too, of all people! imagine the bewildered way in which he would begin the part of Othello, without in the least knowing how—without so much as an Ethiopian dye to help him out. You must allow that in writing to you I have done all I could; more, I do believe and hope, than there was any need of my doing; but I look to your goodness and affection for your brother to excuse me. I want merely to suggest that you should keep a quiet friendly watch over Frank so as to save him any distress or difficulty in the future. A sister rather older and wiser than himself ought really to be about the best help and mainstay a boy of his age can have. If I had had but five years or so more to back me I might have saved your father some scrapes at that time of life.

I have one more petition to my dear niece: be as patient with my garrulous *exigeance* as you can. If you see Reginald Harewood this winter, as I dare say you will—he is pretty sure to be at

Lidcombe before the month is out—may I beg your *bienveillance* towards the poor boy? he is *sat upon* (as he says) just now to such an extent that it is a real charity in any one to shew him a little kindness. I know his brilliant college career is not a prepossessing episode in his history; but so many boys do so much worse—and come off so much better! That insufferable Capt. Harewood behaves as if every one else's son had made the most successful studies and at the end of three years saved up a small but decent income out of his annual allowance. If my father had only had to pay two hundred for the college debts of yours! I cannot conceive what parents will be in the next generation: I am sure we were good-natured enough in ours, and you see what our successors are.

If Mr. Radworth has spare time enough, in the intervals of his invaluable labours, to be reminded of an old woman's unprofitable existence, will you remember me to him in the kindest way? and if you have toiled through my letter, accept the love and apologies of your affectionate aunt?

∼

2.

Mrs. Radworth to Francis Cheyne.

Blocksham, Jan. 16*th*

My dear Frank—If you had taken my advice you would have arranged either to stay up at Oxford during the vacation, or at least to be back by the beginning of next term. Of course we should like of all things to have you here as long as you chose to stay, and it would be nicer for you I should think than going back to fog and splashed snow in London: but our half-engagement to Lidcombe upsets everything. Ernest is perfectly restless just now; between his dislike of moving and his wish to see the old Lidcombe museum again he does nothing but *papillonner* about the house in a beetle-headed way instead of sticking to his cob-webs as a domestic spider should. Are you also bent upon Lid-combe? for if you go we do. Make up your mind to that. If you don't, I can easily persuade Ernest that his museum has fallen to dust and tatters under the existing dynasty; which indeed is not so unlikely to be true. Amicia writes very *engagingly* to me, just the sort of letter one would have expected, limp, amiable, rather a smirking style; flaccid condescension: evidently feels herself agreeable and gracious. I am rather curious to see how things get on there. You seem to have impressed people somehow with an idea that during your last visit the household harmony suffered some blow or other which it has not got over yet. Is there any truth in the notion? but of course if there were I should have known of it before now if I were ever to know at all.

I have had a preposterous letter from Aunt Midhurst; the woman is really getting past her work: her satire is vicious, stupid, pointless to a degree. Somebody has been operating on her fangs, I suppose, and extracting the venom. It is curious to remember what one always heard about her wit and insight and power of reading character; she has fallen into a sort of hashed style, between a French novel and a Dickens nurse. It makes one quite sorry to read the sort of stuff she has come to writing, and think that she was once great as a talker and letter-writer—like looking at her grey fierce old face (*museau de louve* as she called it once to me) and remembering that she was thought a beauty. Still you know some people to this day talk about the softness and beauty of her face and looks, and I suppose she is different to them. To me she always looked like a cat, or some bad sort of bird, with those greyish green eyes and their purple pupils.

I need hardly tell you that since you were here last the place has been most dismal. Ernest has taken to insects now; il me manquait cela. He has a roomful of the most dreadful specimens. In the evenings he reads me extracts from his MS. treatise on the subject, which is to be published in the "County Scientific and Philosophical Transactions." C'est réjouissant! After all, I think you are right not to come here more than you can help. The charity your coming would be to me, you must know; but no doubt it would have to be too dearly paid for.

Lady Midhurst tells me that your ex-ally in old days, and my ex-enemy, Reginald Harewood, is to be at Lidcombe by the end of this month. Have you seen him since the *disgraceful* finale of his Oxford studies? I remember having met him a month or two since when I called on *her* in London, and he did not seem to me much improved. One is rather sorry for him, but it is really too much to be expected to put up with that kind of young man because of his disadvantages. I hope you do not mean to renew that absurd sort of intimacy which he had drawn you into at one time.

I am rather curious to see Lidcombe in its present state, so I think we shall have to go; but seriously, if people are foolish enough to talk about your *relations* there, I would not go, in your place. I am not going to write you homilies after the fashion of

Lady M. or appeal to your good feeling on the *absurd* subject; I never did go in for advice. Do as you like, but I don't think you ought to go.

Ernest no doubt would send you all sorts of messages, but I am not going to break in upon the room sacred to beetles and bones; so you must be content with my love and good wishes for the year.

~

3.

Lady Midhurst to Lady Cheyne.

Ashton Hildred, Jan. 24*th*

My dear Child—You are nervous about your husband's part in
the business; cela se voit; but I hardly see why you are to come
crying to an old woman like me about the matter. Tears on paper
are merely blots, please remember: you cannot write them out
gracefully. Try to compress your style a little; be as sententious
as you can; terse complaints are really effective. I never cried
over a letter but once, and then it was over one of my husband's.
Poor good Sir Thomas was naturally given to the curt hard style,
and yet one could see he was almost out of his mind with distress.
I suppose you know we lived apart in a quiet way for the last ten
years of his life. It was odd he should take it to heart in the way he
did: for I know he was quite seriously in love with a *most horrid*
little French actress that had been (I believe she was Irish myself,
but she called herself Mlle des Grèves—*such* a name! I am *almost
certain* her real one was Ellen Graves—a dreadful wretch of a
woman with a complexion like bad fruit, absolutely a greenish
brown when you saw her in some lights); and the poor man used
to whimper about Nanine to his friends in a perfectly abject way.
Captain H. told me so; he was of my friends at that epoch; he was
courting your mother, and in consequence hers also. Indeed, I
believe he was in love with me at the time though I am ten years
older; however I imagine it looks the other way now. When I saw
him last he was greyer than Ernest Radworth. That wife of his
(E.R.'s I mean) is enough to turn any man's hair grey; I assure
you, my dear child, she makes my three hairs stand on end. Her
style is something too awful; like the most detestable sort of
young man. She will be the ruin of poor dear Redgie if we don't

pick him up somehow and keep him out of her way. He was quite the nicest boy I ever knew, and used to make one laugh by the hour: there was a splendid natural silliness in him, and quantities of *verve* and fun—what Mrs. Radworth I suppose calls pluck or go. Still when one thinks she is really breaking Ernest's heart and bringing Capt. Harewood's *first* grey hairs to the grave with vexation, I declare I could forgive her a great deal, if she were only a lady. But she isn't in the least, and I am ashamed to remember she is my niece; her manners are exactly what Mlle Graves's must have been, allowing for the difference of times. I am quite certain she will be the death of poor Redgie. He was always the most unfortunate boy in this earth; I daresay you remember how he was brought up—always worried and punished and beaten about, ever since he was a perfect baby; enough to drive any boy mad and get him into an infinity of the most awful scrapes when he grew up: but I did think he might have kept out of this one. Clara Radworth must be at least six years older than he is. I believe she has taken to painting already. If there was only a little bit of scandal in the matter! but that is past praying for. It is a regular quiet amicable innocent alliance; the very worst thing for such a boy in the world.

I have gone on writing about your poor brother and all those dreadful people and quite forgotten all I meant to say to you: but I really want you to exert your influence over Redgie. Get him to come and stay with you; *at once,* before the Radworths arrive; I wish to heaven he could come here to be talked round. I know I could manage him. Didn't I manage him when he was fourteen, and ran away from home over here and you brought him in? You were delicious at eleven, my dear, and fell in love with him on the spot, like your (and his) old grandmother; and didn't I send him back at once though I saw what a state he was in, poor dear boy, and in spite of you and his mother? My dear, I could cry to this day when I think what a beautiful boy he was to look at, and how hard it was to have to pack him off in that way, knowing as we all did that he would be three quarters murdered when he got home (and I declare Captain Harewood ought to have been put in the pillory for the way he used to whip that boy every day in the week—I firmly believe it was all out of spite to his mother and me); and you all thought me and your father desperately cruel people you know, as bad as Redgie's father; but I was nearly as soft as either of you at heart and after he went away in the gig I cried for five minutes by myself. Never cry in public (that is, of course, *not irrepressibly*) as your mother did then, and if you ever have children don't put your arms round their necks and make scenes; it never did any good and people always get angry for it makes them look fools and they give you an absurd reputation in the boiled-milk line. Your father was quite put out with her after that demonstrative scene with Redgie and it only made matters worse for the boy at parting, without saving him a single cut of the rod when he got home, poor fellow—I never was sorrier for anybody myself, he was such a pretty boy; you ought to re-member: for after all he is your half-brother and might have been a whole one if Capt. H. had not been such a ruffian. Your poor mother never was the best of managers, but she had a great deal to bear.

Here have I got off again on the subject of my stupid old affection for Redgie and made you think me the most unbearable of grandmothers. I must try and show you that there are some sparks of sense left in the ashes of my old woman's twaddle. But do you know you have made it really difficult for me to advise you? You write asking what to do and I have only to think what I want you to avoid; for of course you will do the reverse of what I tell you. And in effect it seems to me to matter very little what you do just now. However, read over this next paragraph; construe it carefully by contraries; and see what you think of that in the way of advice.

Invite Frank to Lidcombe, as soon as the Radworths come; get up your plan of conduct after some French novel—Balzac is a good model if you can live up to him; encourage Mrs. Radworth, don't snub her in any way, let her begin patronizing you again;

she will if you manage her properly; be quite the child with her, and, if you can, be the fool with your husband, but you must play this stroke very delicately, just the least push in the world, so as to try for a cannon off the cushion; touch these two very lightly so as to get them into a nice place for you, and then you must choose your next stroke. I should say, get the two balls into the middle pocket—if I thought there was a chance of your understanding. But I can hear you saying "MIDDLE pocket? such an absurd way of trying at wit! and what does it mean after all?" My dear, there is a moral middle pocket in every nice well-regulated family: always remember and act on this. If Lord Cheyne and Mrs. Radworth, or either of them, can but be got into it quietly, there is your game. The lower pocket would spoil all, however neatly you played for it; but this I know you will never understand. And yet I assure you all the beauty of the game depends on it.

If you don't like this style—I should be very sorry if you did and it would give me the *worst* opinion of your *head*—I can only give you little practical hints on the chance of their being useful. You know I never had any very great liking for my nephew Francis. His father was certainly the stupider of my two brothers; and, my dear, you have no idea what that implies. If you had known your husband's father, your own great-uncle, you would not believe me when I say his brother was stupider. But John was; I suppose there never was a greater idiot than John. Rather a clever idiot too, and used to work (and live) desperately hard on occasion; but, good heavens! And I can't help thinking the children take after him in some things. Clara to be sure is the image of her mother—a portentous image it is, and I do sometimes think one ought to try and be sorry for Ernest Radworth, but I positively can not; and Frank is not without his points of likeness to her. Still the father will crop out as people say now-a-days in their ugly slang. Keep an eye on the father, my dear, and compare him with your husband when he does turn up. I don't want you to be rude to anybody or to put yourself out of the way in the least. Only not to trust either of those two cousins too far. As for

Cheyne's liking for Clara Radworth, I wouldn't vex myself about that. She cares more just now for the younger bird—I declare the woman makes me talk her style. At sixty and a small piece over. There is certainly something very good about her, whatever we two may think. If you will hold her off Redgie while he is in the house (do, for my sake, I entreat of you) I will warrant your husband against her. She will not try anything in that quarter *unless* she has something else in hand. Cheyne is an admirable double; any pleasant sort of woman can attract him *to her,* but no human power will attract him *from you.* There is your comfort —or your curse, as you choose to make it. C. R. would never think of him except as a background in one of her pictures. He would *throw out* Redgie for example beautifully and give immense life and meaning to the composition of her effects. But as I know you will have no other visitor at Lidcombe who is *human* in any mentionable degree I imagine she will rest on her oars—if you do but keep her off my poor Redgie. You see I *want* you to have a sight of them together that you may study and understand her—on that ground *only* I authorize you to invite her and Ernest while Redgie is still with you; (besides you will be better able to help him if you see it beginning again *under your face;*) not in the least because the Radworths' being there is a pretext for inviting Frank Cheyne and Clara a good firescreen for you; à Dieu ne plaise, I am not *quite* such a *liberal* old woman as that.

Did you ever hear of old Mr. Chetwood, who lived here before your grandfather came? it was his son who sold the place. The old man was the most delicious eighty-year-old (or thereabouts) when I was twenty and a young wife. Herbert Chetwood, the son who sold Ashton Hildred, was a nice sort of man and a perfect fool—ruined himself in two years: I knew him well for the last six months or so before his eclipse, and saw it coming ages before he did. But his father was an angel—rococo type; (I don't mean all plumage and puff.) He was a walking pastel; such a beauty it was. He used to tell stories in the sweetest obsolete way. I can smell his court-powder now if I shut my eyes, and the old scents

(French) he used to steep his things in. One of his stories I must give you in writing—or a ruined ghost of one. You are married and I am sixty-one myself now; besides I had the bringing up of you.

The duc de Beaulnes of his day (goodness knows which one that was—he had lived in Paris for centuries) had a wife who was in love with—well, somebody *you* never heard of, but he was a great man in 176- or 177-, whichever it was. M. de Beaulnes was in love as it happened with this man's wife, and they came to some sort of terms on either side—never mind what, my dear child. M. de S∗∗∗ (*nothing human* should induce me to write his name in full, or to give you my reasons) was willing to behave sensibly; unluckily he was not living with his wife and she had principles, as I am sure I hope you have; the truth was she was in love with *him* up to the neck at least. Well, he did manage by some beautiful bit of strategy to get M. de Beaulnes and his wife together; I wish I could remember the details. I rather think the regent's old Mme de Phalaris (who must have been some awful age by that time) was mixed up in it. Dear good old Mr. Chetwood would have given you all the little points of the comedy to perfection, in that sharp soft manner people had then of telling stories, like the most delicate painting; his Conversations ought to have been published, with engravings of Eisen's. It was splendid to hear him touch on his climax, with a sort of *expansive reticence* in his voice—a repressed rapture that hardly so much as hinted itself in a change of accent, when he came to the presentation of M. le duc de B. to madame la marquise de S. Now, my dear, observe; the point of all this is, that it came to nothing; precise, absolute nothing. There was an old stupid mother in the case, just like me; a Mme de Montreuil she was, Mr. Chetwood always called her Madame la présidente (a name that invariably puts me in mind of a most shocking book of that time which I hope you never will dream of reading). This old lady had very good eyes (mine are not bad on the whole) and saw her way through this little matter. She gave her daughter no advice (I daresay you wish I would take example by her in that) but she waited and arranged all the stage furniture for the two chief actors. I can't tell you exactly how things went off; but I know the net result was just nothing at all. M. de Beaulnes and Mme de S∗∗∗ had time to appreciate each other in peace and to find it decidedly not worth while to get up the slightest atom or shadow of an affair. The marquise even gained in reputation as a dévote by her treatment of M. de B. and remained on the most perfect terms with her mother. There was only one thing to regret; M. de S∗∗∗ had his own way and the duchesse de Beaulnes hardly came out of his clutches alive; il l'accommoda d'une belle façon, Mr. Chetwood used to say, but he never would tell me how, and if I have ever guessed since then, *redhot pincers and scalding water* should never get my conjecture out of me. On parle encore, my dear old man wound up, de certain plat découpé à la duchesse de Beaulnes; mais le pis est que Mme la présidente en fut fort aigrie et fit après à son beau-fils un mal affreux; elle l'éxécrait de tout son cœur, ce pauvre cher marquis, et de plus elle aimait fort Mme de Beaulnes dont elle était marraine. And all the rest of her days (the duchesse's I mean) a most horrid nickname stuck to her—the ugliest *female* name in the French language. Mme de Phalaris I believe used always to call her *Petrarch's Laura,* but the other name was a perfectly awful one. Mr. Chetwood never told me what it was, but I found that much out by myself long afterwards, when I took to thinking it over. I really must some day publish recollections and anecdotes of that delicious old man and one or two other people I have known in my time.

Now you see the model I want you to imitate is Mme la Présidente de Montreuil. She was old and you are a girl, but with common sense you ought to manage. Be *light* in your handling of C. R.; give her *play:* it will be a charming education for you. If you do this—even supposing I am wrong about your husband's *devotion* to you—you are sure of him. Item; if you can once *come over* her (but for heaven's sake don't irritate or really frighten her) she will be a capital friend for you. Find out too how her brother feels towards her and write me word that I may form my own ideas as to him. If he appreciates without overrating her there must be some sense in him. She is one of those women who are usually overrated by the men, and underrated by the women, capable of appreciating them. Mind you never take to despising *any* character of that sort—I mean if there *is* a character in the case.

I have written you a shamefully long letter and hardly a word to the point in it I daresay you think: besides I am not at all sure I ought to have written part of it to a good young married woman; there is one comfort, you won't see what I mean in the least. One thing you must take on trust, that I do seriously with all my heart hope and mean to serve you, my dear child, and help you to live well and wisely and happily—as I must say you ought. Do take care of Redgie; I regard that boy as at least three years younger than you instead of three years older. Love to both of you from your mother and

Your very affectionate
H. Midhurst.

~

4.

Francis Cheyne to Mrs. Radworth.

(London) Jan. 25*th*

My dearest Clara—I am off to Lidcombe in a fortnight's time and shall certainly not return to Oxford (if I do at all) till the summer term. I really wonder you should think it worth while to dwell for a second on what Lady Midhurst may choose to say: for I cannot suppose you have any other grounds to go on than this letter of hers; and certainly I do not mean to alter my plans in the least on account of her absurdities. You must remember what our father used to say about her "impotent incontinence of tongue." I should be ashamed to let a vicious virulent old aunt influence me in any way. I am fond of our cousins, and enjoy being with them; it is a nice house to stay at, and as long as we all enjoy being there together I cannot see why we should listen to any spiteful and senseless commentaries. To meet you there will of course make it all the pleasanter; I need not fear that you will take the overseer line with me, whatever our aunt's wisdom may suggest. As to Amicia, I think she is very delightful to be with and fond of us all in a friendly amiable way; and I know she is very beautiful and agreeable to look at or talk to, which never spoils anything; but as to falling in love, you must have the sense to know that nobody over eighteen or out of a bad French novel, would run his head into such a mess: to say nothing of the absurdity or the villainy of such a thing. It all comes of the ridiculous and infamous sort of reading which I have no doubt the dear aunt privately indulges in. I do hope you will never quote her authority to me again, even in chaff. I never can believe that she really had the bringing-up of Amicia in her own hands; it is wonderful how little of the Midhurst mark has been left on *her*. I suppose her father was a nicer sort of fellow to begin with: for as to our cousin Mrs. Stanford, one can hardly suppose that she bequeathed Amy an antidote to her own blood. I am sure her son has enough of the original stamp on him: and I do not wonder at Ly M.'s liking for him, considering. You decidedly need not be in the least afraid of any excessive intimacy between us. Redgie Harewood has been some weeks in town it seems, and I have met him two or three times. I agree with you that he is just what he used to be, only on a growing scale. At school I remember he used simply to *flâner* nine days out of ten and on the tenth either get into some serious row or turn up with a decent set of verses for once in a way. I dare say he will be rather an available sort of inmate at Lidcombe: you will have to put up with him at all events if you go, for I believe he is there already. Really, if you can get on with him at first, I think you will find there are worse fellows going. It appears, for one thing, that his admiration of you is immense. He does me the honour to seek me out rather, with a view I suppose of getting me to talk about you. That meeting here in London after his final flight from Oxford mists in the autumn term, seems to have done for him just now. So if you ever begin upon the subject of Amicia to me I shall retort upon you with that desirable brother of hers. I should like to see old Harewood's face if his son were ever to treat him to such a rhapsody as was inflicted upon me the last time Reginald was in my rooms here.

I start next week, so probably I shall be at Lord Cheyne's before you. Come as soon as you can after me and take care of Ernest. Do as you like for the rest, but pray write no more Midhurst letters at second-hand to

Your affectionate brother
Francis Cheyne.

~

5.

Lady Cheyne to Francis.

You know I hope that we expect your sister and Mr. Radworth in the course of the week? I have had the kindest letter from her, and it will be a real pleasure to see something more of them at last. I have always liked your brother-in-law very much: I never could understand your objection to scientific men. They seem to me the most quiet innocuous good sort of people one could wish to see. I quite understand Clara's preferring one to a political or poetical kind of man. You and Reginald are oppressive with your violent theories and enthusiasms; but a nice peaceable spirit of research never puts out anybody. I remember thinking Mr. Radworth's excitement and delight about his last subject of study quite touching; I am sure I should enter into his pursuits most ardently if I were his wife. It is strange to me to remember I have not seen either of them since they called last at Ashton Hildred a few months before my marriage. I suspect your sister has a certain amount of contempt for my age and understanding: all I hope is that I shall not disgrace myself in the eyes of such a clever person as she is. Clara is one of the people I have always been a little in awe of; and I quite believe if the truth were known you are rather of the same way of feeling yourself. However, I look to you to help me, and I dare say she will be lenient on the whole. Her letter was very gracious.

I suppose you have heard of Reginald's arrival. He is wild at the notion of seeing your sister again; I never saw anybody so excited or so intense in his way of expressing admiration. It seems she is his idea of perfect grace and charm: I am very glad he has such a good one, but he is dreadfully unflattering to me in the mean time, and wants to form everybody upon her model. I hope you are not so inflammable on European matters as he seems to be: but I know you used to be worse. Since he has taken up with Italy there is no living with him on conservative terms. Last year he was in such a state of mind about Garibaldi and the Sicilian business that he would hardly take notice of such insignificant people as we are. My husband has gone through all that stage (he says he has), and is now rather impatient of the sort of thing: he has become a steady ally, on principle, of strong governments. No doubt, as he says, men come to see things differently at thirty, and understand their practical bearing: but nothing will get Reginald to take a sane view of the question, or (as Cheyne puts it) to consider possibilities and make allowance for contingent results. So you see you are wanted dreadfully, to keep peace between the factions. Redgie is quite capable of challenging his half-brother-in-law to mortal combat on the issue of the Roman question.

Lord Cheyne is busy just now with some private politics of his own, about which he admits of no advice. If he should ever take his seat and throw his weight openly into the scale of his party, I suppose neither you nor Reginald would ever speak to either of us? I wish there were no *questions* in the world; but after all I think they hardly divide people so much as they threaten to do. So we must hope to retain our friends as long as they will endure us, in spite of opinions, and make the most of them in the interval. We look for you on the fifth.

Believe me
Ever your affectionate cousin
A. Cheyne.

~

6.

Lady Midhurst to Reginald Harewood.

Ashton Hildred, Feb. 21st

Oh, if you were but five or six years younger! (you *know* you were at school six years ago, my dear boy) what a letter I would write your schoolmaster! Upon my word I should like of all things to get you a good sound flogging. It is the only way to manage you, I am persuaded. I wish to heaven I had the handling of you. When I think how sorry we all were for you when you were a boy and your father used to flog you! you wrote me the comicallest letters in those days, I have got some still. If I had only known how *richly* you deserved it! Captain Harewood always let you off too easily, I have not an *atom* of doubt. How any one can be such a mere schoolboy as you are at your age I cannot possibly conceive. People have no business to treat you like a man. As to the looks even, my dear, you will never have much more hair on your lips and chin than I have on the crown of my head. You are nothing but a great dull dunce of a fifth form boy (lower fifth if you please) and ought to be treated like one. You don't look at things in a grown-up way.

I want to know what on earth took you to Lidcombe when those Radworths were there? Of course you can't say. Now I tell you you had better have put that hairbrained absurd boy's head of yours into a wasp's nest; do you remember a certain letter of yours to me nine years ago about wasps, and what a *jolly good swishing* you got for running your head into a nest of them against all orders? you thought it *no end of a chouse* then (I kept your letter you see; I do keep children's letters sometimes, they are such fun—I could show you some of Amicia's that are perfect studies) to be birched for getting stung, though it was only a nice wholesome counter-irritant; if all the smart had been in your face, I have no doubt you would have been quite ill for a week; luckily your dear good father knew of a counter-cure for inflammation of the skin; well, I can tell you now that what you suffered at that tender age was nothing to what you will have to bear now if you don't *run at once*. Neither the sting of wasps nor the sting of birch rods is one quarter so bad as the hornet's stings and viper's bites you are running the risk of. You will say I can't know that, not having your experience as to one infliction at least; well, as I never was a boy, certainly I never was flogged, to the best of my belief—at all events, not to the same extent as some of my friends used to be; but I have been stung, and I have been talked of; and if any quantity of whipping you ever got made you smart more than the latter process has made me, all I can say is, that between your father and the birch you must assuredly have got your deserts for once, in a way to satisfy even me if I had seen it. I hope you have—once or twice in your younger days; if so, you must have been flogged within an inch of your life.

However that may be, I assure you I have been talked within an inch of mine. More than once. And so will you be if you go on. I entreat and implore you to take my silly old word for it. Of course I am well enough aware you don't mind; boys never do till they are eaten up body and bones. But you really (as no doubt you were often told in the old times of Dr. Birkenshaw) you really must be made to mind, my dear Redgie. It is a great deal worse for a man than for a woman to get talked about in such a way as you two will be. If there was any real danger for your cousin you don't suppose I would let Amicia have you both in the house at once? But as you are the only person who can possibly come to harm through this nonsensical business I can only write to you and bore you to death. I have no doubt you are riding with Clara at this minute; or writing verses—Amicia sent me your last sea-side sonnet—detestable it was; or hunting; or doing something dreadful. It is really excessively bad for you: I wish to goodness you had a profession, or were living in London at least.

[53]

If you could but hear me talking you over with Mr. Stanford! and the heavy smiling sort of way in which he "regrets that young Harewood should be wasting his time in that lamentable manner—believes there was some good in him at one time, but this miserable vie de flâneur, Lady Midhurst (I always bow when he speaks French in his fearful accent, and that stops him), would ruin any boy. Is very glad Amicia should see something of him now and then, but if he is always to be on those terms with his father—most disgraceful" and so forth. Now do be good for once and think it over. I don't mean what your stepfather says (at least the man who ought to have been your stepfather, if your filial fondness will forgive me for the hint), but the way people will look at it in. I suppose I should pique you dreadfully if I were to tell you that nobody in the whole earth imagines for a second that there is a serious side to the business. You are not a compromising sort of person; you won't be for some years as yet; and you *cannot* compromise Clara. She knows that. So does Amicia. So does Ernest Radworth even, or he ought if he has anything behind his spectacles whatever, which I have always felt uncertain of. I wonder if I may venture to give you a soft light suggestion or two about the object of your vows and verse? I take my courage in both hands and begin. C. R. (you will remember I saw nearly as much of her when she was a girl as I did of Amicia, and I have always made a point of getting my nephews and nieces off by heart) is one of the cleverest *stupid* women I know, but nothing more. Her tone is, distinctly, bad. She has the sense to know this, but not to improve it. The best thing I have ever noticed about her is that under these circumstances she resolves to make the most of it. And I quite allow she is very effective, when at her best: very taking, especially with boys. When she was quite little she was the delight of male playfellows; girls always detested her, as women do now. (You may put down my harsh judgment of her to the score of my being a woman, if you think one can be a woman at my age: a thing I believe to be impossible if one has had the very smallest share of brains to start

[54]

with.) She can't be better than her style, but she won't be worse. I prefer Amicia, I must say; but when one thinks she might have been like Lady Frances Law—I assure you I do Clara justice when I recollect the existence of that woman. Or Lucretia Fielding (you must have seen *her* at Lidcombe); but if I had had a niece like that I should have died of her. A rapid something in phobia—neptiphobia would it be? I suppose not, it sounds barbaric, but my Greek was always very shaky; I learnt of my husband; he had been consul at some horrible hole or other; but anyhow, it would have carried me off. In ten days at the outside. And I hope she would have been hanged.

The upshot of all this is just that our dear C. R. is one of the *safest* women alive. Not for other people, mind; not safe for you; not safe by any means for her husband; but as safe for herself as I am. Or as the Queen is. She knows her place and keeps to it; and any average man or woman who will just do that can do anything. She is a splendid manager in her way; a bad, petty, rather unwise way, I must and do think; but she is admirable in it. Like a genre painter. Her forte is Murillo beggar-boys; don't you sit to her. A slight sketch now and then in the Leech sporting manner is all very well. Even a single study between whiles etched in the Callot style may pass. But the gipsy sentiment I cannot stand. Seriously, Redgie my dear, I will not have it. When she has posed for the ordinary *fastish* woman, she goes in for a sort of Madonna-Gitana, a cross of Raphael with Bohemia. It will not do for you.

Shall I tell you the real simple truth once for all? I have a great mind; but I am really afraid you will take to hating me. Please don't, my dear boy, if you can help, for I had always a great weakness for you, honestly. I hope you will always be decently fond of me in the long run, *malgré* all the fast St. Agneses in gipsydom. Well then; she never was in love but once and never will be again. It was with my nephew Edmund: Amicia knows it perfectly; when his father was alive. She fought for the title and the man with a dexterity and vigour and suppleness of intellect

[55]

that was really beautiful in such a girl as she was—delicious to see. I have always done justice to her character since then. My brother would not hear of cousins marrying, probably because he had married one of our mother's French connexions, who must have been a second cousin at least of his own. So Cheyne had to give her up; he was a moral and social philosopher in those days, and an attachment more or less was not much to him: he was off with her in no time. But at one time, take my word for it, he had been on with her, and things had gone some distance; people began to talk of her as Lady Cheyne that was to be. She was a still better study after defeat than while in the thick of her fight. It steadied her for life, and she married Ernest Radworth in six months. Three years after my good brother died, and the year after that I married Edmund to our dear good little Amicia, as I mean to marry you some day to a Queen of Sheba.

When I say Clara's failure steadied her, you know what I mean, it made her much more *fast* and *loud* than she was before —helped in my poor opinion to spoil her style, but that is beside the question; the real point is that it made her sensible. She is wonderfully sensible for a clever person, who is (I must maintain) naturally stupid, or she would have gone on a higher tack alto- gether and been one of the most noticeable people alive. It is exquisite, charming to an old woman, to observe how thoroughly she is up to all the points of all her games. She amuses herself in all sorts of the most ingenious ways; makes that wretch Ernest's life an Egyptian plague to him by constant friction of his inside skin and endless needle-probings of his sore mental places: enjoys all kind of fun, sparingly and heartily at once, like a thoroughly initiated Epicurean; (that woman is an esoteric of the Garden:) and never for an instant slips aside from the strait gate and narrow way, while she has all the flowers and smooth paving of the broad one—at least all the enjoyment of them; or perhaps something better. She is sublime; anything you like; but she is not whole- some. If she were only the least bit cleverer than she is I would never say a word. Indeed, it would be the best training in the world for you to fall into the hands of a real and high genius. But you must wait. Shew me Athénaïs de Montespan and I will allow you *any* folly on her account; but with Louise de la Vallière I will *not* let you commit yourself. You will say C. R. is something better than this last; I know she is; but not enough. If you had ever had your English history well flogged into you, as it should have been if I had had the managing of matters—and I should have if your father had not been the most—never mind—you would have learnt to appreciate her. She is quite Elizabethan, weakened by a dash of Mary Stuart. At your age you cannot possibly understand how anybody can be at once excitable and cold. If you will take my word for that fact, I will throw you another small piece of experience into the bargain. A person who does happen to combine those two qualities has the happiest temperament *imaginable*. She can enjoy herself, her excitability secures that; and she will never enjoy herself too much, or pay too high a price for anything. These people are always exceedingly acute, unless they are absolute dunces, and then they hardly count. I don't mean that their acuteness prevents them from being fools, especially if they have a strong stupid element in them, as many clever excitable people have; notamment ladite Marie, who was admirably and fearfully foolish for such a clever cold intellect as she was. I fancy our friend has more of the Elizabeth in her; quite as dangerous a variety. If she ever does get an impulse, God help her friends; but there will be no fear even then for herself: not the least. Only do you take care; you have not the stuff to make a Leicester; and I don't want you to play Essex to a silvergilt Elizabeth. Silver? she is just pinchbeck all through. As to heart, that is, and style; her wits are well enough.

Now, if you have got thus far (but I am convinced you will not), you ought to understand (but I would lay any wager you don't) what my judgment of her is, and what yours ought to be. She is admirable, I repeat again and again, but she ought not to be adorable to you; the great points about her are just those which appeal to the experience of an old woman. The side of her that a boy like you can see of himself, is just the side he ought not to care about. Of course he will like it if he is not warned; but I have warned you: quite in vain, I am fully prepared to hear. If you are in effect allured and fascinated by the bad weak side of her I can't help it: liberavi animam meam; I suppose even my dunce of the lower fifth (at twenty-three) can construe that. My hand aches, and you may thank heaven it does, or you would get a fresh *dressing* (as people call it) on paper. Do, my dear, try to make sense of this long dawdling wandering scrawl; I meant to be of some use when I began. I don't want to have my nice old Redgie made into a burnt-offering on the twopenny tinselled side-altar of St. Agnes of Bohemia.

I send no message to the Lidcombe people, as I wrote to Amicia yesterday. Give my compliments to your father if you dare. I must really be very good to waste my time and trouble on a set of girls and boys who are far above caring to understand what an old woman means by her advice. You seem to me, all of you, even younger than your ages; I wish you would stick to dolls and cricket. Cependant, as to you, my dear boy, I am always

Your affectionate Grandmother

Helena Midhurst.

P.S. You can shew this letter to dear Clara if you like.

~

7

Reginald Harewood to Edward Audley.

Lidcombe, March 1st

Did you see last year in the exhibition a portrait by Fairfax of my cousin Mrs. Radworth? you know of course I am perfectly well aware the man is an exquisite painter with no end of genius and great qualities in his work; but I declare he made a mull of that picture. It was what fellows call a fiasco: complete. Imagine sticking her into a little crib of a room with a window and some flowers and things behind her, and all that splendid hair of hers done up in some beastly way. And then people say the geraniums and the wainscot were stunning pieces of colour, or some such rot; when the fellow ought to have painted her out of doors or on horseback or something. I wish I could sit a horse half as well; she is the most graceful and the pluckiest rider you ever saw. I rode with her yesterday to Hadleigh, down by the sea, and we had a gallop over the sands; three miles good, and all hard sand; the finest ground possible; when I was staying here as a boy I used to go out with the grooms before breakfast and exercise the horses there instead of taking them up to the downs. She had been out of spirits in the morning and wanted the excitement to set her up. I never saw her look so magnificent; her hair was blown down and fell in heavy uncurling heaps to her waist; her face looked out of the frame of it, hot and bright, with the eyes lighted, expanding under the lift of those royal wide eyelids of hers. I could hardly speak to her for pleasure, I confess; don't shew my avowals. I rode between her and the sea, a thought behind; a gust of wind blowing off land drove a mass of her hair across my face, upon my lips; she felt it somehow I suppose, for she turned and laughed. When we came to ride back, and had to go slower (that Nourmahal of hers is not my notion of what her horse should be—I wish one could get her a real good one) she changed somehow and began to talk seriously at last; I knew she was not really over happy. Fancy that incredible fool Ernest never letting her see any one when they are at home except some of his scientific acquaintance—not a lady in the whole countryside for her to speak to. You should have heard her account of the entertainments in that awful house of theirs—about as much life there as there used to be at my father's—don't I remember the holiday dinners there! a parson, a stray military man of the stodgier kind, my tutor, and the captain: I kept after dinner to be chaffed, or lectured, or examined—a jolly time that was. Well, I imagine her life is about as pleasant; or worse, for she can hardly get out or go about at all. People come there with cases of objects, curiosities, stones and bones and books, and lumber the whole place. She had to receive three scientific professors last month; two of them noted osteologists, she said, and one a comparative ichthyologist or something—a man with pink eyes and a mouth on one side, who was always blinking and talking: a friend of my great-uncle's it seems, who presented him years ago to that insane ass Radworth. Think of the pair of them and of Clara obliged to sit and be civil! She became quite sad towards the end of our ride; said how nice it had been here, and that sort of thing, till I was three quarters mad. She goes in three or four days: I should like to follow her everywhere and be her footman or her groom, and see her constantly. I would clean knives and black boots for her. If I had no fellow to speak or write to, I can't think how I should stand things at all.

~

8.

Francis Cheyne to Mrs. Radworth.

(London) March 15*th*

You don't suppose I want you to quarrel with me, my dear Clara? It is foolish to tax me with trying (as you say) to *brouiller* you with the Stanfords or with Redgie Harewood. As to the latter, you know we are on good enough terms together; I never was hand and glove with him that I recollect. Do as you like about Portsmouth. I will join you if I can after some time.

But about my extra fortnight at Lidcombe I must write to you. Lord Cheyne is quite gracious, with a faint flavour of impertinence; I never saw one side of him before. (Since I left I have heard twice; once from him and once from Amicia. They talk of coming up. Cheyne thinks of beginning to speak again. I believe myself he never got over your cruel handling of his eloquence six years ago. I remember quite well once during the Easter holidays hearing you and Lady Midhurst laugh about it by the hour.) Amicia is, I more than suspect, touched more deeply than we fancied by the things that were said this winter. Her manner is often queer and nervous, with a way of catching herself up she has lately taken to—breaking off her sentences and fretting her lip or hand. I wish at times I had never come back. If I had stayed up last Christmas to read as I thought of doing, there would have been nothing for people to talk of. Now, I certainly shall not think of reading for a degree. Perhaps I may go abroad; with Harewood if I can get no one else. He is the sort of fellow to go anywhere and make himself rather available than otherwise in case of worry.

Tenez, I suppose I may as well say what I meant to begin upon at once, without shirking and fidgeting. Well, you were right enough about my staying after you left; it did lead to scenes. In a quiet way of course; subdued muffled-up scenes. I was reading to her once and Cheyne came in; she grew hot, not very red but hot and nervous, and I caught the feeling of her; he wanted us to go on, and as we began talking of other things left us rather suddenly. We sat quiet for a little and then somehow or other found ourselves talking about you, I think apropos of Cheyne's preferences; and she laughed over some old letter of Lady Midhurst's begging her to take care of Redgie Harewood and prevent his getting desperately in love with you; I said Lady M. always seemed to me to live and think in a yellow paper French novel cover, with some of the pages loose in sewing; then A. said there was a true side to that way of looking at things. So you see we were in the thick of sentiment before we knew it. And she is so very beautiful to my thinking; that clear pale face and full eyebrows, well apart, making the eyes so effective and soft, and her cheeks so perfect in cutting. I cannot see the great likeness of feature to her brother that people talk of; but I believe you are an admirer of his. It was after this that the dim soft patronizing manner of Cheyne's which I was referring to began to shew itself, or I began to fancy it. We used to get on perfectly together, and he was never at all *gracious* to me till just now, when he decidedly is.

Make Radworth come up to London before you go to Portsmouth or Ryde or wherever it is. And do something or other in the Ashton Hildred direction, for I am certain by things I have heard Amicia say that Lady Midhurst "means venom." So lay in a stock of antidotes. I wish there was a penal colony for women who outlive a certain age, unless they could produce a certificate of innocuous imbecility.

~

9

Lady Midhurst to Lady Cheyne.

Ashton Hildred, March 18*th*

So you have made a clear house of them all, my dear child, and expect my applause in consequence? Well, I am not sure you could have done much better. And Cheyne is perfect towards you, is he? that is gratifying for me (who made the match) to hear of: but I never doubted him. As for the two boys, I should like to have them in hand for ten minutes; they seem to have gone on too infamously. I retire from the field, for my part; I give up Redgie; he must and will be eaten up alive, and I respect the woman's persistence. Bon appétit! I bow to her and retire. She has splendid teeth. I suppose she will let him go some day. She can hardly think of marrying him when Ernest Radworth is killed off. If I thought she did I would write straight to Captain Harewood. Do you think the Radworth has two years' vitality left him?

I am too old to appreciate your state of mind as to your cousin. (You know too that I have a weakness for clear accurate accounts, and your style is of the vaguest. It is impossible you can be so very foolish as to become *amourachée* of a man in any serious sense. Remember, when you write in future, that I shall not for a second admit that idea. Married ladies in modern English society *cannot* fail in their duties to the conjugal relation.) Recollect that you are devoted to your husband, and he to you. I assume this when I address you, and you must write accordingly. The other hypothesis is *impossible* to take into account. (As to being in love, frankly, I don't believe in it. I believe that stimulant drinks will intoxicate, rain drench, and fire singe; but not in any way that one person will fascinate another.) Avoid all folly; accept no traditions; take no sentiment on trust. Here is a bit of social comedy in which you happen to have a part to play; act as well as you can, and in the style now received on the English boards. Above all, don't indulge in tragedy out of season. Resolve, once for all, in any little difficulty of life, that there *shall* be nothing serious in it; you will find it depends on you whether there is to be or not. Keep your head clear, and don't confuse things; use your reason: determine that, come what may, nothing shall happen of a nature to involve or embarrass you. As surely as you make this resolution and act on it, you will find it pay.

I must say I wish you had been more attentive to my hint with regard to your brother. Study of the Radworth interior, and the excitement (suppose) of a little counterplot, would have kept you amused and left you sensible. I see too clearly that that affair is going all wrong: I wish I saw as clearly how to bring it all right. Reginald is a hopeless specimen; I never saw a boy so fairly ensorcelé. These are the little pointless endless things that people get ruined by. Now if you would but have taken notice of things you might have righted the whole matter at once. If I could have seen you good friends with Clara I should have been content. But as soon as you saw there was no fear of her making an affair with your husband (or, if you prefer, of his being tolerably courteous to her) you threw up your cards at once. At least you might have kept an eye on the remaining players: and a little interest in their game would have given you something better to think about than Frank. As it is you seem to have worked yourself into a sort of vague irritable moral nervousness which is not wholesome by any means.

I want you to go up to London for some little time, and see the season out. Encourage Cheyne's idea of public life; it is an admirable one for both of you. The worst thing you could do would be to stay down at Lidcombe another month (and then (as you seem to think of doing) join your cousins again in some foolish provincial or continental expedition.) I had hoped to have seen you and Clara pull together, as they say now, better than you do; I have failed in the attempt to make you; but at least, as it seems you two can have no real mutual influence or rational amicable apprehension of each other, I do trust you will not of your own accord put yourself in her way for no mortal purpose. Is it worth while meeting on the ground of mutual indifference? I recommend you on all accounts to keep away from both brother and sister.

Not that I underrate him, whatever you may think. I see he is a nice boy; very faithful, brave and candid; with more of a clear natural stamp on him than I thought. The mother has left him enough of her quick blood and wit, and it has got mixed well into the graver affection and sense of honour that he inherits from our side. I like and approve him; but you must observe that all this does not excuse absurdities on either hand. Of course he is very silly; at his age a man must be a fool or nothing: by the *nothing* I mean a pedant either of the head or the heart species (avoid pedants of the heart kind, by the way), or a coquin manqué. I have met the latter; Alfred Wandesford, your father's friend, was one of that sort at Frank's age; you know his book had made a certain false noise—gone off with a blank report—flashed powder in people's eyes for a minute; and being by nature lymphatic and malleable at once, he assumed a whole sham suit of vices cut out after other men's proportions, that hung flapping on him in the flabbiest pitiable fashion; but he *meant* as badly as possible; I always did him the justice, when he was accused of mere paste-board sins and scenepainters' profligacy, to say that his wicked-ness was sincere but clumsy. It was something more than wickedness made to order. Such a man is none the less a rascal because he has not as yet found out the right way to be a rascal; or even because he never does find it out, and dies a baffled longing scoundrel with clean hands. Wandesford did neither, but turned rational and became a virtuous and really fortunate man of letters, whom one was never sorry to see about: and I don't know that he ever did any harm, though he was rather venomous and vulgar. One or two things of his are still worth your reading.

[65]

Now because Frank is neither a man of this sort, nor of the pedant sort, but one with just the dose of folly proper to his age, and that folly of rather a good kind, I want him not to get entangled in the way that would be more dangerous for him than for any other sort of young man. I wish to heaven there were some surgical process discoverable by which one could annihilate or amputate sentiment. Passion, impulse, vice of appetite or conformation, nothing you can define in words is so dangerous. Without sentiment one would do all the good one did either by principle or by instinct, and in either case the good deed would be genuine and valuable. Sinning in the same way, one's very errors would be comprehensible, respectable, reducible to rule. But to act on feeling is ruinous. Feeling is neither impulse nor principle—a sickly deadly mongrel breed between the two. I hate the very word sentiment. The animalist and the moralist I can appreciate—but what on any ground am I to make of the sentimentalist?

Decide what you will do. Look things and people in the face. Give up what has to be given up; bear with what has to be borne with; do what has to be done. Remember that I am addressing you now with twenty years of the truest care and affection behind me to back up my advice. Remember that I do truly and deeply care about the least thing that touches you. To me you are two; you carry your mother about you.

Let us see what your last letter really amounts to. You have seen a good deal of your cousin for the last six weeks and are vaguely unhappy at his going. (Once or twice, I am to infer, there has been a touch of softer sentiment in your relations to each other.) Not, I presume, that either has dreamt of falling in love: but you live in a bad time for intimacies; a time seasoned with sentiment to that extent that you can never taste the natural flavour of a sensation. You were afraid of Clara too, a little; disliked her; left her to Cheyne or to Reginald as the case might be (one result of which by the by is that I shall have to extricate your brother, half-eaten, from under her very teeth); and let

[66]

yourself be drawn, by a sort of dull impulse without a purpose under it, towards her brother. Purpose I am of course convinced there was none on either side. I should like to have some incidents to lay hold of; but I am quite aware that incidents never do happen. I wish they did; anything rather than this gradual steady slide of monotonous sentiment down a groove of uneventful days. The recollection that you have not given me a single incident,—nothing by way of news but a frightened analysis of feeling and record of sentimental experience—makes me seriously uneasy. Write again and tell me your plans: but for heaven's sake begin moving; get something done; engage yourself in some active way of amusement. Have done with the country and its little charities and civilities—at least for the present. London is a wholesomer and more reasonable home for you just now.

~

10.

The same to the same.

Ashton Hildred, April 6*th*

Well, I have been to London and back, my dear child, with an eye to the family complications, and have come to some understanding of them. When I wrote to you last month I was out of spirits, and no doubt very stupid and obscure. I had a dim impression of things being wrong, and no means of guessing how to get them right. Now I must say I see no real chance of anything unfortunate or unpleasant. You must be cautious though of letting people begin to talk of it again. I have a project for getting both the boys off on some good long summer tour, well out of the way. Frank is very nice and sensible; I would undertake to manage him for life by the mere use of reasoning. As to Reginald, c'est une tête fêlée; it may get soldered up in ten years' time, but wants beating about first; I should like to break it myself. Actually I had to encourage his verse-making, pat that Rigolboche of a Muse of his on the back (don't repeat my similies, please)—and stroke him down with talk of publication till he purred under my fingers. It is a mercy there is that escape-valve of verse. I think, between that and his sudden engouement for foreign politics and liberation campaigns and all that sort of thing, he may be kept out of the worst sort of mess: though I know one never can count upon that kind of boy. I should quite like to enrol him in real earnest in some absurd *legion* of volunteers and set him at the quadrilateral with some scores of horrid disreputable picciotti to back him. I daresay he would fight decently enough if he were taken into training. Imagine the poor child in a red rag of a shirt, and shoeless, marching *au pas* over the fallen dynasties to the tune of a new and noisier Marseillaise. It would serve him right to get rubbed against the sharp edges of his theory, and if he were killed we should have a mad martyr in the family, and when the red republic comes in we might appeal to the Committees of Public Safety to spare us for the sake of his memory. His father would die of it, for one thing; I do think Redgie is fated to make him *crever* with rage and shame and horror; so you see I shall always have a weak side in the boy's favour. But if you knew how absurd all this recandescence of revolution in the young people of the day does seem to me! My dear Amy, I have known men who had been dipped in the old revolution.

J'ai connu des vivants à qui Danton parlait.

You remember that great verse of Hugo's; I shewed it to Reginald the last time he was declaiming to me on Italy, and confuted him out of the master's mouth. It is true of me, really; both my own father and my dear old friend Mr. Chetwood had been in Paris at dangerous times. They had seen the great people of the period, and the strange sights of it. Mr. C. had a wonderful story of an escape of his; he was laid hold of somehow I think by some Committee of Pikes, and brought off by one man's intervention—the secretary's of the committee I believe; I shall not tell you how or why, indeed I hardly know. Others were saved in as strange a way and by the same hand. The times were strange (as somebody says), and brought forth strange men and things.

I have run off into all this talk about old recollections and forgotten as usual my starting-point; I was thinking of the last interview I had with Reginald. But I suppose you want some account of my stay in London. You know I had your house to myself (it was excellent on Cheyne's part to renew his offer of lending it and spare an ancient relative the trouble of asking you to get her the loan of it from him): and as your father came up with me I travelled pleasantly enough, though we had fearful companions. I rested for a day or two, and then called upon the

Radworths. Ernest looks *fifty;* if he had the wit to think of it, I should say he must always have understated his real age. I have no doubt though he will live for ages (I don't mean his reputation but his bodily frame). Unless indeed she poisons him: I am certain she would if she durst. She herself looks older; I trust in a year or two she will have ceased to be at all dangerous, even for boys. We had a curious interview; not that day, but a week after. I saw Reginald next day; he is mad on that score, quite. I like to see such a capacity for craziness, it looks as if a man had some corresponding capacity for being reasonable when his time came. He never saw such noble beauty and perfection of grace, it appears; there is an incomparable manner about the least thing she does. She is gloriously good, too; has a power of sublime patience, a sense of pity, a royal forbearance, a divine defiance of evil, and various qualities which must ennoble any man she speaks to. To look at her is to be made brave and just; to hear her talk is a lay baptism, out of which the spirit of the auditor comes forth purged and with invulnerable armour on; to sit at her side is to become fit for the grandest things: to shake hands with her makes one feel incapable of a mean wish. Base things die of her, she is poisonous to them. All the best part of one, and all that makes a man fit to live, comes out in flower at the sight of her eyes. Accepting these assertions as facts (remarkable perhaps but indisputable) I desired to know whether Ernest Radworth was my friend's ideal of the glorified man? heroic as a martyr he certainly was, I allowed, in a passive way. If a passing acquaintance becomes half deified by the touch of her, I put it to him frankly, what must not her husband have grown into by this time, after six years of marriage? Reginald was of opinion that on him the divine influence must have acted the wrong way. The man being irredeemably base, abject, stupid, there was nothing noble to be called out and respond to her; the only result therefore of being always close to the noblest nature created was in men like him a justly ordained increase of degradation. Those that under such an influence cannot kindle into the superhuman *must,* it seems, harden into the animal. (You will admit I was tempted to quote mythology for the case of Diana: but I abstained.) This, Redgie averred, was his deliberate belief. Experience of character, study of life, the evidence of common sense, combined to lead him unwilling to this awful inference. But then how splendid was her conduct, how laudable her endurance of him, how admirable in every way her conjugal position! I suggested children. The boy went off into absolute incoherence. I could not quite gather his reasons, but it seems the absence of children is an additional jewel in her crown. He is capable of finding moral beauty in a hump and angelic meaning in a twisted foot. And all the time it is too ludicrously evident that the one point of attraction is physical. Her good looks, such as they are, lie at the root of all this rant and clatter. We have our own silly sides no doubt; but I do think we should be thankful we were not born males.

After this specimen of the prevalent state of things I felt of course bound to get hold of her and hear what she had to say. She had a good deal. I always said she could talk well; this time she talked admirably. She went into moral anatomy with the appetite of sixty; and she is under thirty—that I admit. She handled the question in an abstract indifferent way wonderful to see. The whole thing was taken up on high grounds, and treated in a grand spirit of research—worthy of the husband. She did not even profess to regard Redgie as a brother—or friend. In effect she did not profess anything; a touch of real genius, as I thought at once. He amused her; she liked him, believed in him, admired his best points; altogether appreciated the value of such a follower by way of change in a life which was none of the liveliest. Not that she made any complaint; she is far too sharp to poser à l'incomprise. I told her the sort of thing was not a game permitted by the social authorities of the time and country; the cards would burn her fingers after another deal or two. She took the hint exquisitely; was evidently not certain she understood, but had a vague apprehension of the thing meant; fell back finally upon a noble self-reliance, and took the pure English tone. The suggestion of any harm resulting was of course left untouched: such a chance as that we were neither of us called upon to face. The whole situation was harmless, creditable even. Which is perfectly true, and that is the worst of it. As in most cases of Platonism, there is something to admire on each hand. And the existence of this single grain of sense and goodness makes the entire affair more dangerous and difficult to deal with. She is very clever to manage what she does manage, and Reginald is some way above the run of boys. At his age they are usually made of soft mud or stiff clay.

When we had got to this, I knew it was hopeless dissecting the matter any further, and began talking of things at large, and so in time of her brother and his outlooks. She was affectionate and hopeful. It seems he has told her of an idea which I encouraged; that of travelling for some months at least. How tenderly we went over the soft ground I need not tell you. Clara does not think him likely to be carried off his feet for long. Console yourself, if you want the comfort; we have no thought of marrying him. He is best unattached. At the present writing he no doubt thinks more of you than *she* would admit. I regret it; but he does. Do you, my dear child, take care to keep out of the way just now. I hear (from Ernest Radworth; his wife said nothing of it; in fact when he began speaking the corners of her mouth and eyelids flinched with vexation—just for a breath of time) that there is some talk now of a seaside summer expedition. Redgie of course; Frank of course; the Radworths, and you two. I beg you not to think of it. Why on earth should you all lounge and toss about together in that heavy way? You are off to London at last, or will be in ten days' time you say; at least, before May begins. Stay there till it breaks up; then go either north or abroad. Yachts are ridiculous; and I know you will upset yourself. To be sure sentiment can hardly get mixed into the situation if you do. The soupir entrecoupé de spasmes is not telling in a cabin; you sob the wrong way. Think for a second of too literal heartsickness.

Cheyne is fond of the plan, it seems: break him of that leaning. He and Redgie devised it at Lidcombe, Ernest says; (he has left off saying Harewood; not the best of signs; fœnum habet—never mind how tied on; if he does go mad we will adjust it; but I forget I never let you play at Latin. Rub out this for me; I never erase as you know, it whets and frets curiosity; and I can't begin again.)

Frank, when I saw him, pleased me more than I had hoped. I made talk to him for some time; he is unusually reticent and rational; a rest and refreshment after that insane boy whom we can neither of us drive or hold as yet (but I shall get him well in hand soon, et puis gare aux ruades! kick he will, but his mouth shall ache and his flanks bleed for it.) No show or flutter of any kind; a laudable peaceable youth, it seems to me. Very shy and wary; would not open up in the least at the mention of you: talked of his sister very well indeed. I see the points of resemblance now perfectly, and the sides of character where the likeness breaks down. He is clever as well as she, but less rapid and loud; the notes of his voice pleasant and of a good compass, not various. I should say a far better nature; more liberal, fresher, cleaner altogether, and capable of far more hard work. Miss Banks comes out in both their faces alike though. Corrected of course by John: which makes her very passable.

Is there much more to say? As you must be getting tired again, I will suppose there is not. Will you understand if I suggest that in case of any silent gradual breach beginning between Cheyne and Frank you ought to help it to widen and harden in a quiet wise way? I think you ought. I don't mean a coolness; but just that sort of relation which swings safe in full midway between intimacy and enmity. We all trust you know that he is never to be the heir; you must allow us to look for the reverse of that. Then, don't you see yourself, it must be best for him to get a good standing for himself on his own ground, and not hover and *flicker* about Lidcombe too much? I know my dear child will see the sense of what I say. Not, I hope and suppose, that she needs to see

[73]

it on her own account. Goodnight, dearest; be wise and happy: but I don't bid you trouble your head overmuch with the heavy hoary counsels of

Your most affectionate
H. M.

~

11.

Reginald Harewood to Mrs. Radworth.

(London) April 15*th*

You promised me a letter twice; none has come yet: I want the sight of your handwriting more than you know. Sometimes I lie all night thinking where you are: and sometimes I dare not lie down for the horror of the fancy. If I could but entreat and pray you to come away—knowing what I do. Even if I dared hope the *worst* of all was what it cannot be—a hideous false fear of mine—I could hardly bear it. As it is I am certain of one thing only in the world, that this year cannot leave us where the last did. If I must be away from you, and if you must remain with him, I cannot pretend to live in the way of other men. It is too monstrous and shameful to see things as they are and let them go on. Old men may play with such things if they dare. We cannot live and lie. You are brave enough for any act of noble justice. You told me once I knew you to the heart and ought to give up dreaming and hoping—but I might be sure you said of what I had. I do know you perfectly, as I love you: but I hope all the more. If *hope* meant anything ignoble, could I let it touch on you for a moment? I look to you to be as great as it is your nature to be. It is not for myself—I am ashamed to write even the denial—that I summon you to break off this hideous sort of compromise you are living in. What you are doing insults God, and maddens men who see it. Think what it is to endure and to act as you do! I ask you what right you have to let him play at husband with you? You know *he* has no right; why should you have? Would you let him try force to detain you if your mind were made up? You are doing as great a wrong as that would be if you stay of your own choice. Who could blame you if you went? who can help blaming you now? I say you cannot live with him always. If I thought you could, could I think you incapable of baseness? and you know, I am certain you do in your inmost heart know, that you have shewn me by clear proof how infinitely you are the noblest of all women. Do all prefer a brave and blameless sorrow with the veil close over it to a shameful sneaking happiness under the mask? There was a time when I thought I could have worn it if I had picked it up at your feet. The recollection makes me half mad with shame. To have conceived of a possible falsehood in your face is degradation enough for me. Now that you have set me right (and I would give my life to shew you how much more I have loved you ever since) I come to ask you to be quite brave. Only that. I implore you now to go without disguise at all. You cannot speak falsely I know; but to be silent is of itself a sort of pretence. Speak for heaven's sake, that all who ever hear of you may adore you as I shall. Think of the divine appeal against wrong and all falsehood that you will be making! a protest that the very meanest must be moved and transformed by. It is so easy to do, and so noble. Say why you go, and then go at once. Put it before your brother. Go straight to him when you leave the hateful house you are in. He is very young I know, but he must see the greatness of what you do. Perhaps one never sees how grand such things are—never appreciates the reality of their grandeur—better than one does at his age. I think boys see right and wrong as keenly as men do; he will exult that you are *compelled* to turn to him and choose him to serve you. As for me, I must be glad enough if you let me think I have taken any part in bringing about that which will make all men look upon you as I do—with a perfect devotion of reverence and love. I believe you will let me see you sometimes. I would devote my whole life to Radworth—give up all I have in the world to him. Even *him* I suppose nothing could comfort for the loss of you; but if it ought to be! At least we would find something to do. I entreat you to read this, and answer me. There can be but one

[76]

answer. I wish to God I knew what to do that you would like done, or how to say what I do know—that I love you as no woman ever has been loved by any man. What to call you, or how to sign this, I cannot think. I am afraid to write more.

R. E. H.

~

12.

Answer to the above.

My dear Cousin—One word at starting; I must not have you think I feel obliged to answer you at all. I do write, as you see; but not because I am afraid of you. And I am not going to pretend you put me out. You shall not see me *crane* at the gaps. Your fences are pretty full of them. Seriously, what can you mean? What you want I know. But how can you hope I am to listen to such talk? Run away from nothing? I see no sort of reason for changing. You take things one says in the oddest way. I no more mean to leave home because Ernest and I might have more in common, than I should have thought of marrying a man for his beaux yeux—or for a title. I hate hypocrisy. You are quite wrong about me. Because I am simple and frank, because I like (for a change) things and people with some movement in them, you take me for a sort of tied-up tigress, a woman of the Sand breed, a prophetess with some dreadful mission of revolt in her, a trunk packed to the lid with combustibles and labelled with the proof-mark of a new morality: not at all. I am neither oppressed nor passionate. I don't want delivering in the least. One would think I was in the way of being food for a dragon. Even if I were, how could you get me off? We are born to what we bear; I read that and liked it a day since, in de Blamont's last book. I mean to bear things. We all make good packhorses in time: I shall see you at the work yet. Suppose I have to drudge and drag. Suppose I am fast to the rock with a beast coming up "out of the sad unmerciful sea." Better women live so, and so they die. Can you kill my beast for me? I suspect not. It is not cruel. It means me no great harm: but you it will be the ruin of. It feeds on the knight rather than

[78]

his lady. Do you pass by. Be my friend in a quiet way, and always. I shall be gratefuller for a kind thought of yours than for a sheer blow. The first you can afford; the last hardly. All goodwill and kindly feeling does give comfort and pleasure to natural people who are not of a bad make to begin with. I am glad of any, for my part: and take it when I can. What more could you do for me? what better could I want? Can you change me my life from the opening of it? It began before yours was thought of; you know I am older; have been told how much, no doubt; something perhaps a thought over the truth; what matter?

I will tell you what I would have done if I could get it. I would begin better; I would be richer, handsomer, braver, nicer to look at and stay near, pleasanter to myself. I would be the first woman alive, and marry the first man: not an Eve though, nor Joan of Arc nor Cleopatra, but something new and great. I would live more grandly than great men think. I should have all the virtues then, no doubt; and I would have all I wanted, and the right and the power to feel reverence and love and honour of myself into the bargain. And my life and death should make up "a kingly poem in two perfect books." That would be something better than I can make my life now. I dare say I might have had a grander sort of man for my companion than I have (a better I think hardly); but then I might have been born a grander sort of woman. There is no end to all that, you see. I am very well as I am; all the better that I have good friends.

I began as lightly as I could, and said nothing of your tone of address and advice being wrong or out of place; but now you will let me say it was a little absurd. Your desire seems to be that, because I have not all I might have (whereas I also am not all I might be), I should leave my husband and live alone, in the cultivation of noble sentiments and in vindication of female freedom and universal justice. How does it sound to you now? I do not ask you if such a proposal ever was made before. I do not even ask you if it ought ever to be listened to. I make no appeal to the opinions of the world. I say nothing of the immediate unavoidable consequences. Suppose I can go, and (on some grounds) ought to go. Are there not also reasons why I ought to stay? Reflect for a minute on results. Think, and decide for yourself, whether I could leave Ernest. For no cause. Just because I *can* leave him, and like to shew that I *know* I can. I ask you, is that base or not? I should be disgracing him, spoiling his life and his pleasure in it, and using my freedom to comfort my vanity at the cost of his just self-esteem and quiet content; both of which I should have robbed him of at once. I will do no such thing. I will not throw over the man who trusted and respected me—loved me in a way—gave me the care of his life. When he married me, he reserved nothing. I have been used generously; I have received, at all events, more than I have given. I wish, for my own sake chiefly, that I had had more to give him. But what I have given, at least I will not take away.

No, we must bear with the realities of things. We are not the only creditors. Something is due to all men that live. How much of their due do you suppose the greater part of them ever get? Was it not you who shewed me long ago that passage in Chalfont's Essays where he says—I have just looked it out again—my copy has a slip of paper at the page with your initials on it—

"You are aware the Gods owe you something, which they have not paid you as yet—all you have received at their hands being hitherto insufficient? It appears also that you can help yourself to the lacking portion of happiness. Cut into the world's loaf then, with sharp bread-knife, with steady hand: but at what cost? Living flesh as sensitive of pain as yours, living hearts as precious as your heart, as capable of feeling wrong must be carved and cloven through. Their blood, if you dare spill it for your own sake, doubtless it shall make you fat. They too want something; take from them all they have, and you shall want nothing. At this price only shall a man become rich even to the uttermost fullness of his desire; that he shall likewise become content—to rob the poor."

Ah, after the reading of such words as those, can we turn back to think of our own will and pleasure? dare we remember our own poor wants and likings? I might be happier away from here; what then, my dear cousin? I might even respect myself more, feel more honourable; and this no doubt is the greatest personal good one can enjoy or desire; but can I take from the man who relies on me the very gift that I covet for myself? A gift, too, this one, which all may win and keep who are resolved not to lose it by their own fault. I for one, Reginald, will not throw it away; but I will not rob others "to heighten my relish of it with the stolen salt of their life." Do you remember that next bit?

"And suppose now that you have eaten and are full; digesting gravely and gladly the succulence and savour of your life. Is this happiness that you have laid hold of? Look at it; one day you will have to look at it again; and other eyes than yours will. The terror of a just judgment is this, that it *is* a just one. The sting of the sentence is that you, your own soul and spirit, must recognize and allow that it is rightly given against you. Fear not the other eyes, not God's or man's, if what is done remain right for ever in your own. Few, even among cowards, are really afraid of injustice. The meanest of them are afraid mainly of that which does at first sight look just. But is this right in your eyes, to have cut your own share out of the world in this fashion? But what sort of happiness, then, is this that you have caught hold of? The fairest, joyfullest, needfullest thing created is fire; and the fist that closes on it burns. Let go, I counsel you, the bread of cunning and violence, the sweet sauces of treason and self-seeking; there are worse ends than the death of want. A soul poisoned is worse off than a starved soul."

You used to praise this man to me, saying there was no grander lover of justice in the world. Surely to such a writer liberty and truth are as dear as to you or me: and this is what he advises. An American too, as he says himself, fed with freedom, full of the love of his own rights; but all great men would say as he says, and all good men would do so. I shall try at least. "There is an end of time, and an end of the evil thereof; and when joy is gone out of

[81]

thee, then shall not thy sorrow endure for long. Nevertheless thou sayest, grief shall remain with me now that I have made an end of my pleasure; but grief likewise shall not abide with thee. For before the beginning a little sorrow was ordained for thee, and also a very little pleasure; but there is nothing of thine that endureth for ever."

Do you know where I found that? in a book of my husband's, the *Sayings of Aboulfadir,* in a collection of translations headed *The Wise Men of the East.* You see I am growing as philosophic as need be, and as literary. We know better than that last sentence, but is not the rest *most true?* You will forgive my preacher's tone; it was hopeless trying to answer such a letter as you wrote me in a sustained light manner.

I hope you are not put out with me; I may say now, in ending, how sorry I should be for that. You must find other things to think of, without forgetting or throwing over old friendship. "Plenty of good work feasible in the world somehow" says your friend. For my poor little part, I have just to hold fast to what I have, and at least forbear doing harm. Again I ask you to forgive me if this letter has hurt you anywhere. Of course you can *never* shew it. Farewell.

～

13.

Francis Cheyne to Lady Cheyne.

(London) May 7th

I have read your letter twice over carefully, and cannot see why we should alter our plans. My sister I know counts upon you. But I can imagine from what quarter the objection comes: and I hardly like to think you will let it act upon you in this way. Indeed I for one have promised your brother to meet him halfway, on the understanding that we were all to be at Portsmouth or Ryde together. He for one would be completely thrown out, if our project were to break up. Is Lord Cheyne tired of the plan do you think? if so I suppose there is no more to say. You speak so uncertainly of "having to give it up" and "not being sure of the summer" that I have perhaps missed out some such hint. Of course a word must be enough for us, but I fear it will not be easy to get over Reginald. He is hot on the notion; I think he must have a touch of the sea-fever. In our school days he used to bewail his fate in having been cut off from the sea as a profession; I can remember when he would hang over the idea for whole days. At one time we all expected him to be off some day; I believe the masters were half afraid he would, too.

(May 8th)

I left off yesterday because I wanted to go on differently. Now, as I mean to finish this and send it off at all hazards, I must speak out fairly once for all. I do not think you can mean to break with all our hopes and recollections, and change the whole look of life for me. I do not suppose you have more regard for me than for any other kinsman or chance friend. And I do not appeal to you on the score of my own feeling. You are no coward to be afraid of words, or of harmless things. I can say safely, that if I could die to save you trouble or suffering I should thank God. I love nothing now seriously that does not somehow belong to you: all that does not seems done in play, or to get the time through. But I am not going to plead with you on this ground. I ask nothing of you; if you were to die to-night I should still have had more than my fair share of luck in life. If I am to see you again, I can only be as glad of it as I am now, when I think of you. I cannot understand why I should not have this too to be glad of. What can people say, as things are? unless indeed there were to be a change of appearances. Then they might get vicious, and talk idiocy. But you know what I should do. It is not I who have to set you right: we neither of us want stupid words, or anything like the professional clack of love.

I think sometimes you might come to care for me a little more. I know you detest *that*. Perhaps the last word above had no business where it came in. I remember your way of saying what things you hated.

I see Reginald often now; I suppose he is all right. I am fond of him, but don't envy his way of taking things. I like to look at him and make out why he is thought so like you: and I think when he is with me he talks more of you than he used. I can hardly think he is older than I am when I see how much less he knows or feels of one thing.

(May 9*th*)

I have let this lie over another day. I have nothing to say but that I *can* say nothing. When I begin to write I seem to hear you speaking. I believe at times I can tell by the sensation what you are doing at Lidcombe. I have heard you speak twice since I sat down: and I know the dress you have on. Do not write unless you want. I can see how you will take this. I cannot help it, you understand. There is Reginald's knock; but this shall go to-day, and I will not touch it again.

~

14.

Lady Midhurst to Reginald Harewood.

Ashton Hildred, May 12*th*

My dear Boy—You are without exception the best fun I know. I have been laughing for the last two hours over your letter and its enclosure. You are not to fly out at me, mind; I regard you with all just esteem, I think all manner of good things of you, but you *are* fun, you will allow. Old friends may remark on such points of character and yet draw no blood.

Now, my dear Redgie, what do you think I got by post exactly three days before this epistle of yours with Clara's valuable bit of English prose composition so neatly inserted? I am humane and will not let your brains tingle with curiosity even for a minute. I got *this;* a note (not ill worded by any means) from my affection-ate and anxious niece C. R. enclosing your last letter to her. She threw herself upon me (luckily the space between us softened the shock of her weight, enabling me to bear up) with *full* confidence and gratitude. I could explain and advise. I could support and refresh. I was to say whether she were right or no. To Mr. Radworth she would not turn for sustenance or counsel. Ought a wife to—would a wife be justified if she did—do so and so? Through all this overture to her little performance one could hear thrill the tone of British matronhood, tremulously strong and tenderly severe. I did think it was all over with some of you: but found rapid relief. She put it to me; was she to notice it? was she to try to bring you to reason, appealing to the noble mis-managed nature of you? Could she treat your letter as merely insulting or insane? My private answer came at once—Decidedly she could not; but I never wrote it down—it went off in a little laugh, quietly. She wound up with an intimation that I was thus taken into confidence in order to give me a just and clear idea of *her* conduct and position—this she owed to herself (the debt was well paid and I receipted it by return of post), but she would rather say as little of your folly as she could avoid. Of course she put it twice as prettily, and in a very neat soft way; but I give you the real upshot. She understood—Clara you see did—that I felt warmly and fondly towards you; she was aware that I could not but know the way in which your conduct would affect her, Clara; and on your account, on mine, (by no means I need not say on her own) she now felt—various things in the sensation line eminently creditable to her.

I drew breath after this, and then laid hold of your letter. It did not upset me, you will like to hear. Indeed I compliment you on the fervour of such a "selfless and stainless" form of devotion. You play Launcelot in a suit of Arthur's armour—rather in his new clothes after the wellknown make of modern tailordom, which I grieve to see are already cast wear, or how should you come by them? The vividness and loftiness of view throughout is *idyllic*. In effect, considering your heat of head and violence of sentiment, I think you behave—and write—nicely, nobly even, if you like to be told so. It is right you should take things in the way you do, now you are first plunged into them. I am glad you do persuade yourself of the justice and reality of your passionate paradoxes and crude conceptions about social rights and wrongs. Naturally, being in love, like the bad specimen you are, you find institutions criminal and revolt desirable. It is better, taking your age into account, than trying to "sneak" under shelter of them within reach of the forbidden fruits. Storm the place if you can, but no shooting behind walls; a good plan for you, as I am glad you see. Altogether, if you are cracked, I should say you had no unsound side; a fool you may be, but you get through your fooleries like a gentleman. *You* are "brave enough" too, as you said; it was no coward's letter, that one. I should not forgive you otherwise, but I was always sure so far of my old Redgie: you never had any of the makings of a coward about you. I like the hopeless single-sighted daring of your proposals: also your way of feeling what disgrace would be. Except in the vulgarest *surface* fashion she for one will never understand that—never get to see the gist of your first few lines, for instance. I do; but don't you get on that ground again, my dear boy. I like you all the better; and that has nothing to do with it, you see. In a word—allow that you were outside of all reason in writing the letter, and I will admit you have kept well inside the lines of honour. So far there is nothing to forgive (which is tant soit peu lowering); and not much to punish (which is at worst painful). There is a school copy for you: make me an exercise in C.'s style on that head.

So much for you; now for her side; and I do beg you to read this patiently, and do me justice as far as you can. You send me her answer to your letter in a rapture of admiration, with a view of altering and ennobling my estimate of her, which you know to be hitherto of a moderate kind. I am to read and kindle, acknowledge and adore. Is she not noble?—Let us see.—Ought we not to do honour to such grand honesty and purity, such a sublime goodness?—I am not over sure.—You write to me as to your first best friend (and effectively, my dear old child, I don't think you have a better one—I do feel *parental* on your score) wishing to set my mistakes right and bring me to an equitable and generous tone of mind: you do me the honour to think me capable of conversion, worthy to worship if I did but see the altar as it really stands. Being such as I am I cannot but appreciate greatness and high devotion if I can but be brought face to face with them. That I think is what you mean, or rather what you had floating in your head when you wrote to me.—Well, we must hope you were right; I am no doubt flattered, and will try to be deserving.—Then, I must now see things as you do, and admit the sublimities of behaviour you have made out in C. R. to be real discoveries and not flies in your telescope. Her noble letter to you—a letter so fearless of misconception, so gently worded, so devoted and so just—must compel me to allow this much.—Wait; you shall have my poor verdict as to that by and by.

[87]

But now, what have you to say about her letter to me? Why do you suppose she sends me your epistle to her? I should like to know. To me, honestly, it does seem like a resolution to be quit of all personal damage or risk or other moral discomfort; also, it does seem very like a keen apprehension—very laudably keen —of a chance given her to right herself or to raise herself in my judgment by submitting the whole matter to me. I, as arbitress, must decide, on receiving such an appeal from her backed by such proofs, that she had gone on splendidly—was worthy of all manner of praise—and that you, as a crazy boy in the "salad days" of sentiment, were alone blameworthy. Now, frankly, do you believe she had any other meaning? Why need she appeal to me at all? Certainly I am her nearest female relation. Après? And we have always been on the nicest terms. What then? There was no call for her to refer to anybody. She is old enough, at all events (and *that* she will hardly deny, or insinuate a denial of), to manage by herself for herself. Do you imagine she wrote on your account? applied to me for your sake? I do not. How could I help her? how could I settle you? Favour me by considering that. One thing I could do, and that she knew well enough. I could change my mind as to her (she was always clever enough to know what my honest opinion of her was) and prevent, by simply expressing approval if not applause of her, any chance of annoyance she might otherwise have run the risk of. Do you see? it was no bad stroke; just the kind of sharpness you know I always gave her credit for. Very well played too by forwarding me your letter; she was aware I should hardly have relied on extracts or summaries of her making, and was not such a fool as to appeal to me in a vague virtuous way. Upon the whole, as it seemed to her, she could not fail to come out admirably from the test in my eyes. I confess, for the sort of woman, she is far-sighted and sharp-sighted. Only, there is one thing to be taken into account; that I have known both her and you since you were the tiniest thinking animals possible. She was not hard upon you; not in the least. I was to draw all the inferences for myself.

And now for her letter to you. Luckily I had read all this before I came to it. And after all I am surprised: not admiringly by any means. I looked for better of her, considering. As she could not decently assume alarm or anger, and was not the woman to write in the simple Anglican fashion, you see there was nothing for it but to mix audacity with principle. She begins fairly on that score: the opening is not bad. But how could you swallow the *manner?* was there ever such a way of writing? The chaff as you others call it is so poor, so ugly and paltry: the tone of rebuke such a dead failure; the air of sad satisfaction so ill put on; the touches of sentiment so wretchedly coloured. I wonder she could do no better; she gets up her effects with trouble enough, and is not a fool. As to the magnanimous bits—I do really want to know if it has *never* crossed your mind for a second that they were absolute impertinences? Were you *quite* taken in by that talk about "man who trusted and respected," "just self-esteem," "used generously," and such like? "Received more than she has given!" "not the only creditor"! Why, my poor boy, I tell you again she married the man tooth and nail; took him as a kite takes a chaffinch. Certainly he wanted her; but as to having wind enough to run her down! It upsets me to write about it. Throw him over! It is perfect impudence to imagine she can make any living creature above twelve suppose that regard for Ernest keeps her what one calls a good wife. She looks it when you come upon them anywhere. But your age has no eyes. Sense of duty? she cares for the duties and devotions no more than I should care for her reputation if she were not unhappily my relative. It is a grievous thing to see you taking to such a plat d'argot réchauffé. For pure street slang it is, not even the jargon of rational society. Do you know what ruin means? or compromise even? And she is not the woman, by nature or place, to risk becoming *tarée* in the slightest degree. She is thoroughly equable and cautious, beyond a certain point. The landmark is a good bit this side of serious love-making; hardly outside the verge of common sentiment. I assure you there is nothing to be made of her in any other way.

She will keep you on and off eternally to no further purpose.

Upon the whole I don't know that her letter could well have been a worse piece of work than it is. Why, if you would but observe it, she runs over into quotation before getting a good start; and I never saw this modern fashion of mournful satirical *introspective* writing more ungracefully assumed. Her sad smiles *crack,* and show the enamel. You know how an old wretch with her face *glazed* looks if she ventures to laugh or cry? at least you can imagine if you will think of me with a coating of varnish on my cheeks and lips, listening to you for five minutes. Well, just in the same way the dried paint of her style *splits* and spoils the whole look of her letter at the tender *semi-rident* passages. It is too miserably palpable. Don't you see her trying to write up to tradition? say what she has to say in the soft pungent manner she thinks proper to her part as a strong-minded, clear-headed, virtuous, somewhat *rapid* humourist (don't suppose I meant to write *vapid*), with a touch of the high-minded unpretentious social martyr? I must tell you of a bit of verse I kept thinking of while I ran over this epistle of hers—Musset you know—

Triste! oh, triste en vérité!
—Triste, abbé? Vous avez le vin triste?

If you had but the wit to take it in that way, and answer her accordingly! Elle a l'amour triste, like most of her sort. For you must allow she is making love, though in the unpractical way. If I could but see an end of this dolorous kind of verbal virtue and compromised sentiment—this tender tension of the moral machine, worse for the nerves than the headiest draughts of raw sensation! But it all comes of your books; I thank heaven we were reared on sounder stuff. Confess that her American sermons were almost too much for you. As for Aboulfadir, I never was so nearly hysterical since the decease of your grandfather. I *actually*

[90]

saw her looking out the bit. And your initials on the slip of paper, you remember? Oh, you utter idiot!

Allow me one more question before you tear me up. Has it yet struck you what her last words *mean?* "You can *never* shew this:" that is, in heaven's name forward this to old Aunt Midhurst next time she writes spitefully about me.—Now, Reginald, I will not have bad language. You know she meant that; the woman capable of inditing that letter must be capable of thinking it good enough to influence *any* reader, upset *any* prejudice. You were to send it (you must admit you did) and it was to complete the grand work of refutation begun a week before by her appeal to me on the occasion of *your* letter. Now I do hope you see; it was really a passable stroke of wit. The whole thing was cooked with a view to its being served up stewed in the same sauce. No doubt, after the great conception, her brain swelled with the sense of supreme diplomacy. Perhaps a man might have been taken in. Evidently a boy was. For my part I think it personally insulting to have supposed my opinion of her was to be affected by such a cheap specimen of the scene-shifter's professional knack. I see as well as ever how she wants to play her hand out.

I give you a month, my dear boy, to get over your rage at me; then I shall expect you to behave equably. Till that time I suppose I must let you "chew the thrice-turned cud of wrath." Otherwise I should beg you not to make one of the south-coast party I hear of. Also if you did go to stick close to your sister. As it is I see you will join the rest, and waste your time and wits, besides sinking chin-deep in Platonic sloughs of love. Some day I may succeed in pulling you out. I dare say it ought to be a comfort to me to reflect that you are doing no great harm; dirtier you might get, but scarcely wetter. The quagwater of sentiment will soak you to the bone. In earnest, if you go to Portsmouth or elsewhere with the Cheynes, you are to let me hear now and then. I hope there is enough love or liking between us two to stand a little sharp weather between whiles. Even though I *am* unbearably vicious and shamefully stupid with regard to your cousin, you ought to try and overlook it. Recollect my age, I entreat you. Can you expect sound judgment and accurate relish of the right thing from such an old critic as I am? You might as well hope to make me see her beauty with your eyes as appreciate her goodness in your fashion. And then, bad as I may be, we have been friends too long to break off. If I had ever had a son in my younger years, things would have gone differently: as it was, I have always had to put up with you instead. A bad substitute you make, too; but somehow one gets used to that. If I could have taken you with me from the first and reared you under shelter of your mother (nice work I should have had of it by the by; but all *that* labour fell to your father's share), I would have broken you in better. I would, regardless of all expense in birch; though as to that the captain did his duty by you liberally, I will say. When you were born I could not realize your mother's age to myself in the least; I myself was only thirty-eight (look me out in the dates if you won't take my word for it), and I could not make her out old enough to have a son. Besides I had always hungered after a boy. So I took to you from the beginning in an idiotic way, and by this time no doubt my weakness is developing into senile dotage. I don't say I always stood by you: but you must remember, my dear Redgie, I could not always. Your ill luck was mine as to that, and your mother's too. I wish I could have kept by you when you did want some of us at hand: not that I suppose the softest-hearted boy feels deeply the want of a superincumbent grandmother. Still we should all have got on the better for it, I conceive. No doubt too I have not always done the best for you—only *my* best: but that I did always want to do. In a word, you know I love you as dearly as need be: and you may as well put up with me for fault of a better.

Take this into account when you feel furious, and endeavour to make the best you can of me. I perceive this letter is running to seed, and my tattle fast lapsing into twaddle. After all I don't suppose my poor shots at the pathetic will bring down much game of the sentimental kind. I might bubble and boil over with feeling long enough (I suspect) before you melted. Besides, what does it matter, I should be glad to know? However, I do trust you will be as good a boy as you can, and not bring me to an untimely grave in the flower of my wrinkles.

~

15.

Lady Cheyne to Francis.

(Portsmouth) May 28th

Do not write; and do not persist in trying to speak to me again. If you care for any of us you will not stay here. I can do nothing. When my husband speaks to me it turns me hot and sick with fear. I am ashamed of every breath I draw. If you cannot have mercy, do for God's sake think of your own honour. If you stay here, you may as well shew this letter at once. I wish Cheyne would kill me. But even if he saw what I am thinking of when I look at him I believe he would not. He is so fearfully good to me. Oh, if I were to die I should never forget that. I don't know that it matters much what I do. I have broken my faith to him in thought, and if justice were done I ought to be put away from him. I look at my hand while I write, and think it ought to be cut off: my ring burns. I cannot think how things can be so dreadful as they are. I suppose if I can live through this I shall live to see them become worse. If I could but see what to do I should be content with any wretchedness. I never meant to be a bad wife. When I woke this morning I felt mad. People would say there was nothing to repent of: but I know. It is worse not to love him than it would be to leave him. What have you done to me? for I never lied and cheated till now. After such horrible falsehood and treason I don't see what crime is to stop me. If I had known that another woman was like me at heart I could not have borne to let her look at me. I feel as if I *must* go away and hide myself. If only something would give me an excuse for going home! At least if I must stay with my husband I implore you to leave me. Tell your sister you *must* go. Say you are tired. Or go to London to-morrow with Cheyne and don't return. You can so easily excuse yourself

[94]

from the sailing party. He stays in town one night, and comes down in time for it the day after. You can make a pretext for remaining. If you have any pity you will. I have nothing to help me in the world. It would kill me to appeal to Reginald. No one could understand. I am sure if you knew how I do want and trust to be kept right, and what a fearful life I have of it with this sense of a secret wearing me out, you would be sorry for me. And if you love me so much, knowing what you know now, you ought to be sorry. It is too late for me to get happy again, but I may come not to feel such unbearable shame as I do now, and shall while you stay. Promise you will not try to see me. I wonder if God will be satisfied, supposing you never do see me again. I shall have tried to be good. I think he ought to have pity on me, too. But if I live to grow old I shall want to see you then.

∼

16

Mrs. Radworth to Lady Midhurst.[1]

Portsmouth, June 3*rd*

You will have heard, my dear aunt, of our wretched loss and the fearful bereavement of our poor Amicia. I wish I could give a reassuring account of her, but she appears to be quite broken: it is miserable to see her. She sits for whole hours in her own room, I did hope at first it was to seek the consolations of prayer, but that comfort I fear greatly she is not yet capable of feeling. She looks quite like *death*. I suggested she should go into the room where he is lying and take her last sight of him, but she turned absolutely whiter than she was, shuddered and seemed quite sick. My brother is hardly less overcome. On a servant addressing him yesterday by his title, he actually *sank* into a chair and gave way in a manner which I could not but regret. I am certain he would sacrifice *worlds* to restore his cousin to life. [2]

Mr. Harewood has been *throughout* MOST KIND. He has done all that the best friend of our *poor child* could do. Amicia will hardly see any one but him. Mr. Radworth offered to relieve him of some part of the wretched trouble and business he has undertaken, to spare dear Amicia (Francis, I must tell you, seems incapable of moving); but he refuses to share it. I cannot express to you the admiration we *all* feel for his *beautiful* management of her, poor child. Who could remember at such a time the former

---

1) All the letters addressed to her on the event of her nephew's death Lady Midhurst, contrary to her custom, carefully preserved for reference.

2) Here a jagged flourish of the pen has scored out half the sentence, but not so as to leave it illegible. The same hand (no doubt Lady Midhurst's) has appended a sort of pothook, between ? and !

folly which he must himself have forgotten?[1] I am constantly reminded that you *alone* always did him justice.

I suppose you will wish to know the sad detail, and it had better perhaps be given at once by me than by another. We had decided, as you know, to take Saturday last as the day of our projected sail. Francis seemed curiously unwilling to go at first, and it was only at poor Lord Cheyne's repeated request that he assented. Amicia was very quiet and I thought rather depressed; I have no doubt in consequence of the reaction from a continued strain on her spirits. It was a very dull party altogether, only Mr. Harewood and poor Edmund seemed to have any spirits to enjoy it. They talked a great deal, especially about summer plans. Quite suddenly we heard ahead what I fancied was the noise of the overfalls, and began passing out of smooth water. I thought it looked dangerous but they *would* put inshore. Feeling the waves run rapidly a little higher and higher, I said something to Amicia, who I knew was a bad sailor, and as she scarcely answered but lay back in the boat I feared the discomfort to her of rough water had begun. I stooped forward, as well as I remember, to sign to my husband to make Lord Cheyne look at her. Ernest, in his nervous absent way, failed to catch my meaning and in rising to speak to me was pitched forwards with a jerk and came full against Mr. Harewood who was helping to shift a sail. Then I really saw nothing more but that the sail yard (is it a yard that they call the bit of wood a sail is tied to?[2]) swung round and I screamed and caught hold of Amicia and *next second* I saw poor Lord Cheyne in the water. He caught at Francis who was next him and missed. Mr. Harewood jumped in after him with his coat on but he could hardly make the least way because of the groundswell. They had to pull him in again almost stifled, and I feared insensible. Before I came to myself so as to see what anybody was doing they had

---

1) Underlined by Lady Midhurst.

2) Note (? by Lady Midhurst) "Too ingenuous by half for the situation."

got the body on board and Francis and the sailors and Ernest were trying to revive it. Amicia, who was shaking dreadfully, kept hold of her brother, chafing and kissing his face and hands. How we ever got back God knows. Amicia seemed quite stunned, she never so much as touched her husband's hand. When we came to get out I thought Francis and my husband would have had to support her, but Mr. Radworth was *quite* useless and poor Francis could not bear even to look at her misery. So Mr. Harewood (who was really unfit to walk himself) and one of the sailors had to carry her up to the house. The funeral takes place to-morrow, I trust my brother may be able to attend, but really he seems at times perfectly broken down in health and everything.

~

17.

Lady Midhurst to Lady Cheyne.

Ashton Hildred, June 6*th*

My dearest Child—I would not let your mother go, or she would have been with you before this. It *must* have done her harm. She is not well enough even to write; we have had to take her in hand. It is a bad time for us all; we must live it down as we best may. I thought of advising your father to be with you before the funeral, but *she* would hardly like him to leave her. I shall start myself to-morrow, and take you home with me. You had better not go to Lidcombe. With us you will at least have thorough quiet, and time to recover by degrees. Now no doubt you are past being talked to. I only hope those people do their best for you. It is well now that nothing ever came between poor Cheyne and you. I suppose you have had as quiet and unbroken a time since your marriage as any one ever does get. The change is sharp; all changes are, that turn upon a death. I know too that he loved you very truly and was always good, just, and tender to all he knew; a man to be seriously and widely regretted. It may be that you are just now inclining to believe you will never get over the pain of such a loss. Now in my life I have lost many people and many things I would have given much to keep. I have repented and lamented much that I have done, and more that has happened to me—sometimes through my own fault. But one thing I do know, and would have you lay to heart; that nobody living need retain in his dictionary the word *irretrievable*. Strike it out, I advise you; I erased it from mine long ago. Self-reproach and the analysis of regret are most idle things. Abstain at least from confidences and complaints. Bear what you have to bear steadily, with locked teeth as it were. This minute may be even graver than you think.

I know how expansion follows on the thaw of sudden sorrow. Mind what I used to tell you when you had hurt yourself as a child; étanchez, n'épanchez pas. I am always ready to hear and help you to the best of my poor old power; but even to me I would not have you overflow too much. I write in all kindness and love to you, my poor child, and I know my sort of counsel is harsh, heathen, mundane. I can hardly help your way of looking at it. No one is sorrier than I am; no one would give more to recall irrevocable things. But once again I assure you, what cannot be recalled may be retrieved. Only the retrieving must come from you. Show honour and regard to Cheyne's memory by controlling and respecting yourself to begin with. If you have some floating desire to make atonement of any kind, atone in that way. But if you have any such feeling, there is a morbid nerve; you should labour to deaden it—by no means to stimulate.

I am more thankful than I can say that you have Reginald with you. The boy is affectionate, and not of an unhealthy nature. He ought to be of use and comfort; I am sure he is good for you. I can well believe you see no more of others than you can help. It was nice for me to hear from any quarter that Redgie had done his part well. There ought always to be a bond between you two. Family ties are invaluable—where they are anything: and neither of you could have a better stay in any time of need than the other. As to friendships of a serious nature (very deeply serious that is) between man and man or between woman and woman, I have no strong belief in their existence: none whatever in their possible usefulness.

I shall be with you in two days at latest; will you understand, if I ask you to wait for me? Till I come, do nothing for yourself; say nothing to anybody. For your mother's sake and mine, who have some claim to be thought of. I add no other name; I don't want to appeal on any grounds but these; but you know why you should spare *her*. Restraint and reserve at present will be well made up to you afterwards. I can imagine you may want some one to lean upon; I daresay it is hard now to be shut up and self-reliant; but I would not on any account have you *expand* in a wrong direction. I could wish to write you a *softer-toned* letter of comfort than this is; but one thing I must say; do not let your grief hurry you even for one minute beyond the reach of advice. As for comfort, my dearest child, what can I well say? I have always hated condolence myself: where it is anything, it is bad—helpless and senseless at best. A grievous thing has happened; we can say no more when all comment has been run through. To us for some time—I say to us, callous as you are now thinking me—the loss and the misfortune will seem even greater than they are. You have the worst of it. Nevertheless it is not the end of all things. The world will dispense with us some day; but it shall not, while we can hold out. Things must go on when we have dropped off; but while we can, let us keep up with life. These are cold scraps enough to feed regret with; but they are at least solid of their kind, which is more than I would say of some warmer and lighter sorts of moral diet. As for what is called spiritual comfort, I would have you by all means take and use it if you can get it, and if the flavour of it is natural to you. I know the way most people have of proffering and pressing it upon one; for my part I never pretended to deal in it. I know only what I think and feel myself; I do not profess to keep moral medicines on hand against a time of sickness. Heaven knows I would give much, or do much, or bear much, to heal you. But indeed at these times, when one must speak (as I now have to do), I prefer things of the cold sharp taste to the faint tepid mixtures of decocted sentiment which religious or verbose people serve out so largely and cheaply. I may be the worse comforter for this; but to me comments either pious or tender usually leave a sickly sense after them as of some flat unwholesome drug. I am not preaching paganism; I would have you seek all reasonable comfort or support wherever it seems good to you. But I for one cannot write or talk about hopes of reunion, better life, expiation, faith, and such other things. I believe that those who cannot support themselves cannot be supported. Those who say they are upheld by faith, say they are upheld by a kind of energy natural to them. This I do entirely allow; and a good working quality it is. But any one who is utterly without self-reliance *will* collapse. There *can* be nothing capable of helping the helpless. So you must be satisfied with the best I can give you in the way of comfort.

I see well enough that I am heathenish and hard. But I know your trouble is a great one, and I will not play with it. It would be easy to write after the received models, if the thing were not so serious. Time will help us; there is no other certain help. Some day when you are old enough to reconsider past sorrows you will admit that there was a touch of truth in my shreds of pagan consolation. Stoicism is not an exploded system of faith. It may be available still when resignation in the modern sense breaks down. Resign yourself by all means to the unavoidable; take patiently what will come; refuse yourself the relaxation of complaint. Have as little as you can to do with fear or repentance or retrospection of any kind. Fear is unprofitable; to look back will weaken your head. As to repentance, it never did good or undid harm. Do not persuade yourself either that your endurance of things that are is in any way a sacrifice of Christian resignation offered to the supreme powers. That is the unhealthy side of patience; the fortitude of the feeble. Be content to endure without pluming yourself on a sense of submission. For indeed submission without compulsion can never be anything but the vicious virtue of sluggards. We submit because we must, and had better not flatter ourselves with the fancy that we submit out of goodness. If we could fight our fate, we all would. It is not the desire to resist that we fail in, but the means; we have no fighting material. It would not be rebellion, but pure idiocy or lunacy, for us to begin spluttering and kicking against the pricks: but on the other hand, that is no reason why we should grovel and blubber. It is a child's game to play at making a virtue of necessity. I say that if we could rebel against what happens to us, we would rebel. Christian or heathen, no man would really submit to sorrow if he could help it. Neither you nor I would, and therefore do not try to believe you are resigned as people call it to God's will in the strict religious sense. For if submission means anything that a Stoic had not, it means something that no one ever had or ought to have. Courage, taking the word how you will, I have always put at the head of the virtues. Any sort of faith or humility that interferes with it or impairs its working power, I have no belief in.

But above all things, I would have you always keep as much as you can of liberty. Give up all for that; sacrifice it to nothing; to no religious theory; to no moral precept. All slavishness, whether of body or of spirit, leaves a taint where it touches. It is as bad to be servile to God as it is to be servile to man. Accept what you must accept, and obey where you must obey; but make no pretence of a "free-will offering." That sort of phrase and that sort of feeling I hold in real abhorrence. Weak people and cowards play with such expressions and sentiments just as children do with tin soldiers. It is their substitute for serious fighting; because they cannot struggle, they say and believe they would not if they could; most falsely. Give in to no such fancies: cherish no such forms of thought. Liberty and courage of spirit are better worth keeping than any indulgence in hope and penitence. I suppose this tone of talk is unchristian; I know it is wholesome though, for all that. God knows our scope of possible freedom is poor and small enough; that is no reason why we should labour to circumscribe it further. We are beaten upon by necessity every day of our lives; we cannot get quit of circumstances; we cannot better the capacities born with us; all the less on that very account need we try to impair them. Because we are all purblind more or less, must we pluck out our eyes and be led about by the ear? Is it any comfort, when we look through spectacles that shew us nothing but shapeless blurs and blots, to be told we ought to see clearly by their help, and must at least take it for granted that others do? Rather I would have you endure as much as you can; repent of as little as you can, and hope for as little as you can. All wise and sober courage ends in that. Do, in heaven's name, try to keep free of false hopes and feeble fears. Face things as they are;

think for yourself when you think of life and death, joy and sorrow, right and wrong. These things are dark by the nature of them; it is useless saying they can be lit up by a candle held in your own eyes. You are only the blinder; they are none the clearer. What liberty to act and think is left us, let us keep fast hold of; what we cannot have, let us agree to live without.

This is a strange funeral sermon for me to preach to you across a grave so suddenly opened. Only once or twice in the many years of one's life the time comes for speaking out, if one will see it. These are matters I seldom think over and never talk about, wishing to keep my head and eyes clear. But my mind was made up, if I did write to you, to keep back nothing I had to say and affect nothing I had not to say. You are worth counsel and help, such as I can give; the occasion too is worth open and truthful speech. I do not pray that you may have strength sent you; you must take your own share of work and endurance; you have to make your strength for yourself. I say again, time will help you, and we shall survive this among other lamentable things. But for me, now that I have said my say and prayed my prayers over the dead, I shall not preach on this text again. What my love and thought for you can do in the way of honest help has been done. If you want more in this time of your danger and sorrow you will not ask it of me. Suppose I were now dying, I could not add a word more to leave you by way of comfort or comment. For once I have written fully, and shewn you what I really think and look for as to these matters. I shall never open up again in the same way to any one while I live. I have unpacked my bag for you; now I put it away for good, under lock and seal. When we meet, and as long as we live together, let us do the best we can in silence.

I add no message; all that would be said you know without that. It could only weaken you and sharpen the pain of the day to you to receive tender words and soft phrases copied out to no purpose. I have told your mother she had best not write: forgive me if you regret it. Indeed I doubt whether she would have tried. When you are here we must all manage to gain in strength and sense. If this letter of mine strikes cold upon your sorrow, I can but hope you may find in good time something or some one able really to soothe and support you better than I can. Meantime if you read it with patience I hope it may help to settle you; save you the useless self-torture of penitent perplexity, and the misery of a fretted retrospect; and lighten your head at all events of some worry, if it cannot just now affect you at heart for the better, as other comforters might profess to do. No one to my thinking can help the heart. There I suppose you must suffer at present. How things are to go with us later on I cannot say or see. But while you live, and whatever you do, believe at least in the love I have for you.

~

18.

Lady Midhurst to Francis Cheyne.

Ashton Hildred, July 20*th*

My dear Frank—I would not have you write to Amicia about those minor arrangements you speak of. Matters had better be settled with me, or by means of your sister. We know you will do all you can in the best possible way; and she is not yet well enough to bear worry. I fear indeed that she has more to bear physically than we had thought of. She keeps getting daily more white and wretched: and we hardly know how to handle her. When she arrived she had a sort of nervous look of strength which begins now to fail her completely; spoke little except to me, but fed and slept like a *rationally* afflicted person. Now I see her get purplish about the eyes and her cheeks going in perceptibly. It will take years to set her straight, if this is to go on. She is past all medicine of mine. I dare say she will begin to develop a spiritual tendency: she reads the *unwholesomest* books. The truth is she is far too young to be a widow. That grey and cynical condition of life fits well only upon shoulders of thirty or forty. She is between shadow and sun, in the dampest place there is. Mist and dew begin to tell upon her brain: there is the stuff of a conversion in her just now. I tell you this because you have known her so well and been such good friends with her that you will be able to take my meaning. I am sure you do want to hear, and sincerely wish all things right with her again. I hope they may be in time; we must take them as they are now. Meantime it is piteous enough to see her. She comes daily to sit with me for hours, and has a way of looking up and sighing betweenwhiles which is grievous to me. Again at times I seem to have glimpses of some avowal or appeal risen almost to her lips, and as suddenly resigned. Her words

[106]

have tears in them somewhere even when she talks *peaceably*. I had no suspicion of so deep and keen a regard on her part. Our poor Edmund can hardly have given her as much, one would say. But who knows what he had in him? he was strange always, with his gentle cold manner, and had rare qualities. "I forget things," she said one day on a sudden to me; I never know what she does think of. Another time; "I wish one could see backwards."

I am glad you went at once to Lidcombe, you will make them a good lord there. Edmund always hung loose on the place. Some day I suppose you will have to marry, but you are full young as yet. I should like to see what the house will hold in ten years' time, but do not much expect the luck. Early deaths age people who hear of them. I feel the greyer for this month's work. They tell me you have had Captain Harewood to help you in settling down and summing up. As he was in a manner your guardian for a year or two after the death of your father I suppose he is the man for such work. I believe he had always a good clear head and practical wit. That wretched boy of his doubtless lost his chance of inheriting it through my fault. We came in there and spoilt the blood. I fancy you have something of the same good gift. It is one I have always coveted, and always failed of; that ready and steady capacity for decisive work. Your mother was a godsend to our family: we never had the least *touch* of active sense among us. All my brother's, now, was loose muddled good sense, running over into nonsense when he fell to work. The worst of him was his tendency to vacuous verbose talk; he was nearly as long-breathed, and as vague in his chatter, as I am. Not such a thorn in the flesh of correspondants, though, I imagine. I hear Reginald is with his father, at Plessey. The place is just endurable in these hot months, but always gives me a notion of thawing time and webbed feet. It is vexatious being unable to send for the boy here; Amy would be all the better for him: but of course it is past looking for. She talks of him now and then in a very tender and grateful way. "Redgie was very good; I wonder what his wife will be?" she said once. There was no chance of such luck for him in sight, I suggested; but she turned to me with singular eyes and said; "I should like her, if she would marry him soon." She has a carte de visite of him, which is made much of. Her husband never would sit for one, I recollect. It seems Redgie was useful when nobody else could have done much good. Those few days were hideous. I never shall forget that white *dried* face of hers, and the heavy look of all her limbs. Poor child, I had to talk her into tears. She had the ways of old people for some time after. Even now she is bad enough; worse, as I told you, in some things. It is great amiability to express such feelings about *turning her out* as you do. No help for it, you know. She would have had more to bear at Lidcombe: and you will soon fit well into the old place. Very fond of it she certainly was and some day perhaps I may take her over to see you. That will be years hence. Your wife must be good to the dowagers: I daresay she will. It will be curious to meet there, anyhow. One thing is a pity, that Amicia can never have a child to keep her company: for I think she can hardly marry again, young as she is. A daughter would have done you no harm, and left her with one side of life filled up: she would have made a perfect mother. I used to think she had much of the good social type of Englishwoman. It is such a broken-up sort of life that one antic-ipates for her. And there was such a tender eager delight in affection, such a soft and warm spirit, such pure pleasure in being and doing good—it is the most delicious nature I know. But you know her too. Love to your sister from both, if she is still with you. Or did they leave when the Plessey people went?

~

19.

Francis Cheyne to Mrs. Radworth.

Lidcombe, July 26*th*

I do not see how I can possibly stay here. If you had not gone so soon, we might have got on: now it is unbearable. There is a network of lawyer's and overlooker's business to be got through still. I go about the place like a thief, and people throw my name in my face at every turn like a buffet. And I keep thinking of Amicia: her rooms have the sound of her in them. I went down to the lake at sunset and took a pull by myself. The noise of the water running off and drawing under was like some one that sobs and chokes. I went home out of all temper with things. And there was a letter waiting from Aunt Midhurst that would have made one half mad at the best of times. She is right to strike if she pleases; but her sort of talk hits hard. I felt hot and sick with the sense of meanness when I had done. These things are the worst one has to bear. She tells me what to do; gives news of Amicia that would kill one to think of if thoughts did kill; mixes allusions in a way that she only could have the heart to do. I believe she knows or thinks the worst, and always has. And there is nothing one can say in reply to her. It is horrid to lie at her mercy as we do. Their life in that house must be intolerable. I can see Amy sitting silent under her eyes and talk; sick and silent, without crying, like a woman held fast and forced to look on while some one else was under torture. I know so well by myself how she must take the suffering: with a blind bruised soul, and a sort of painful wonder and pity; divided from herself; beaten and broken down and tired out. If she were to go mad I should know why. And I cannot come near her, and you know how I love her. I would kill myself to save her pain, and I know she is in pain hourly, and I sit here where she used to be. If I had never been born at all she would have been happy enough with her husband alive. I tell you, God knows how good she was to him. If only one of their people here would insult me, I should be thankful. But the place seems to accept me, and they tolerate a new face; I did think some one would shew vexation or sorrow—do or say something by way of shewing they remembered; I was quixotic, I suppose, for all the old things made way for me. Except the one day when Redgie Harewood came over with his father: he did seem to think I had no business here, and I never liked him so well. You recollect how angry it made you. People ought to remember. I was glad he would not stay in the house. That was the only time any one has treated me as I wanted to be treated. I shall come and stay with you if you will have me. I cannot go about yet and I hate every corner of this house. When I ride, I do literally feel now and then tempted to try and get thrown. Last winter we were all here together, and she used to sing at this time, in this room. Her voice and the sound of her dress come and go in my hearing. I see her face and all her hair glitter and vibrate as she keeps singing. Her hands and her throat go up and down, and her eyes turn and shine. Then she leaves off playing and comes to me and I cannot see her near enough; but I feel her hands touch me, and hear her crying. I can do nothing but dream in this way. I want my life and my love back. I am wretched enough now, and she must be unhappier than I am; she is so much better. Her beautiful tender nature must be a pain to her of every day. I suppose she is sorry for me. I would die to-day if it could make her forget. My dear sister, you must let me write to you as I can, and not mind what I say. I could not well write to a man now: and I never was friends enough with any one to open out as I can to you. I must get strength and sense in time, or make an end somehow. I wish to God I could give all this away and be rid of things at once.

~

20.

Reginald Harewood to Lady Cheyne.

Plessey, Aug. 31st

I was over at Lidcombe again last week. Frank was to leave to-day for his sister's: the Radworths have asked him for some time. I am also pressed to go but I hardly like being with him. Unfair I suppose, but reasonable when one thinks of it. He is a good deal pulled down, and makes very little of his succession: asks after you always, and seems rather to cling to company. All the legal work is over: and I hope you will not be bothered with any more letters. If you care to hear, I may tell you there is some chance of my getting to work after all. They want to diplomatize me; I am to have some secretaryship or other under Lord Foth-erington. If anything comes of it I shall leave England next month. I shall have Arthur Lunsford for a colleague and one or two other fellows I know about me. A. L. was a fearful swell in our school-days and used to ride over the heads of us lower boys with spurs on. I wonder if Frank remembers what a tremendous licking he got once for doing Lunsford's verses for him *without* a false quantity, so that when they were shown up he was caught out and came to awful grief? I don't know if I ever believed in anything as I did once in the get-up of that fellow. To have him over one again will be very comic; he never *could* get on without fags. Do you think the service admits of his licking them? I suspect he might thrash me still if he tried: you know what a splendid big fellow he is. Audley says he is attaché to Lady F. not to the embassy: and makes his way by dint of his songs and his shoulders. People adore a huge musical man. Muscles and music matched will help one to bestride the world. Aimè! I wish I could buy either of them, cheap.

Do you remember an old Mme de Rochelais who used to claim alliance with you through some last-century Cheyne, and was great on old histories? a lank old lady with a half-shaved chin and eyes that our grandmother called vulturine—odd hard eyes that turned on springs in her head without seeming to *look?* She has turned up again this year in England and means to marry her daughter to Frank, the Radworths say. I have seen the daughter and she is admirable; the most perfect figure and hair like the purple of a heartsease; her features are rather too like a little cat's for me; she is white and supple and soft, and I suppose could sparkle and scratch if one rubbed up her fur when the weather was getting electric. Clara thinks her figure must be an English inheritance: she is hardly over seventeen. They do not think Frank will take up with her, though C. would push the match if she could on his account. You would have heard of this from her if I had not written. Mme de Rochelais is two-thirds English you know, and avows her wishes in the plainest way. She is immense fun, and very bland towards me. C'est un jeune démon à pattes de sauterelle, assez joli du reste, she told the Radworths. Complimentary, I hope you admit. She calls Ernest un écolier doublé de son pédant. La seule femme de soixante ans qui n'est ni de bois ni de plâtre, she told me once, c'est cette bonne Lady Midhurst. Toutes les autres péchent par la tête ou boitent par la cheville. Elle seule sait mettre du fard moral sans jurer avec. Tell this; I thought it really good. She gave me one bit of family history which I must send you: it seems she had it from the great-uncle—homme impayable, et dont mon cœur porte toujours le deuil—rapiécé. (She really said it, unprovoked; Frank is a faded *replica* of his father, in her eyes—mais Claire! c'est son portrait vivant—fait d'après Courbet. Which I could not make out; why Courbet? and she would not expound.) Here is the story. The Lady Cheyne of James I.'s time was a great beauty, as we know by that portrait—the one with heaps of full deep-yellow hair, you remember, and opals under the throat. It seems also she was a proverb for goodness, in spite of having to husband that unbeautiful "William, tenth Baron" with the gaunt beard and grisly collar—that bony-cheeked head we always thought the ugly one of the lot. That was why they gave her the motto *Sans reproche* on the frame. She had two fellows in love with her, the one a Sir Edmund Brackley and the other, one regrets to say, the old Reginald Harewood I was christened after, who wrote those poems my father keeps under key and will not let the Herbert Society have to print. I knew he had a story and that the old miniature of him with long curls once had some inscription which my grandfather got rubbed out. He was a fastish sort of fellow evidently, and rather a trump; he had some tremendous duel at nineteen with a Scot of the king's household, and killed his man; never could shew face at court afterwards. The old account was that he lost heart after six months' suit and killed himself for love of her: but the truth seems to be this; that our perfect Lady Margaret lost her own head and fell seriously in love with his rhymes and his sword-hand; and one time (this is the Rochelais version) let him in at a wrong hour. Then in the late night, she went to Lord Cheyne and roused him out of sleep, bidding him come now and be judge between her and all the world. So he got up and followed (in no end of a maze one would think) and she brought him to a room where her lover was lying asleep with his sword unfastened. Then she said, if he believed her good and honest, let him strike a stroke for her and kill this fellow. And the man held off (you should have heard your uncle tell it, Mme de Rochelais said; her own old eyes caught fire and her hand beat up and down); he stood back and had pity on him, for he was so noble to look at, and had such a boy's face as he lay sleeping along. But she bade him do her right, and that did he, though it were with tears. For the lover had hired that night a gentlewoman of hers to betray her into his hands before it was yet day; and she had just got wind of the device. (But really she had let him in herself in the maid's dress, and just then left him. Quelle tête! Mme de Rochelais observed.) Then her husband struck him and roused him and made him stand up there and fight, and before the poor boy had got his tackling ready, ran him through at the first pass under the heart. Then he took his wife's hand and made her dip it in the wound and sprinkle the blood over his face. And the fellow just threw up his eyes and winced as she wetted her hand, and said "Farewell, the most sweet and bitter thing upon earth," and so died. After that she was held in great honour, and most of all by her old suitor Sir Edmund, who became friends with her husband till the civil war when they took up separate sides, and people believed that Brackley (who was of the parliament party) killed Lord Cheyne at Naseby with his own hand. His troopers at all events did, if he missed. The story goes too that Cheyne lived to get at the truth about his wife by means of her servant, and "never had any great joy of his life afterwards." Mme de Rochelais gave me a little copy of verses sent from my namesake "To his most excellent and perfect lady, the Lady Margaret Cheyne;" she got them from our uncle, who had looked up the whole story in some old papers once on a rainy visit at Lidcombe. I copied them for you, thinking it might amuse you when you have time on hand to look them over.

1.

Fair face, fair head and goodly gentle brows,
   Sweet beyond speech and bitter beyond measure;
A thing to make all vile things virtuous,
   Fill fear with force and pain's heart's blood with pleasure;
Unto thy love my love takes flight, and flying
Between thy lips alights and falls to sighing.

2.

Breathe, and my soul spreads wing upon thy breath;
   Withhold it, in thy breath's restraint I perish;
Sith life indeed is life, and death is death,
   As thou shalt choose to chasten them or cherish;
As thou shalt please; for what is good in these
Except they fall and flower as thou shalt please?

3.

Day's eye, spring's forehead, pearl above pearls' price,
    Hide me in thee where sweeter things are hidden,
Between the rose-roots and the roots of spice,
    Where no man walks but holds his foot forbidden;
Where summer snow, in August apple-closes,
Nor frays the fruit nor ravishes the roses.

4.

Yea, life is life, for thou hast life in sight,
    And death is death, for thou and death are parted.
I love thee not for love of my delight,
    But for thy praise, to make thee holy-hearted;
Praise is love's raiment, love the body of praise,
The topmost leaf and chaplet of his days.

5.

I love thee not for love's sake, nor for mine,
    Nor for thy soul's sake merely, nor thy beauty's;
But for that honour in me which is thine,
    To make men laud thee for my loving duties;
Seeing neither death nor earth nor time shall cover
The soul that lived on love of such a lover.

6.

So shall thy praise be more than all it is,
    As thou art tender and of piteous fashion.
Not that I bid thee stoop to pluck my kiss,
    Too pale a fruit for thy red mouth's compassion;
But till love turn my soul's pale cheeks to red,
Let it not go down to the dusty dead.

                Finis.   R. H.

The thing is dated 1625, and he was killed next year, being just my age at the time. I do call it a shame; but Mme de Rochelais says it was worth her while, and would make a good story, which one might call The Cost of a Reputation. Ce sang répandu, voyez-vous, mon enfant, c'était la monnaie de sa vertu. I said I should have preferred it without the small change. Mais, avec de la grosse monnaie, on n'achète jamais rien qui vaille, she said placidly. C'était décidément une femme forte. That is true, I should say, but the presence of mind was rather horribly admirable; she must have had great pluck of a certain sort to go straight off to her husband and put the thing into his head; no wonder they called her Sans reproche. I should put Sans merci on the frame if it were mine. Those verses of his read oddly by the light of the story; I have rather a weakness for that pink and perfumed sort of poem that smells of dead spice and preserved leaves; it reads like opening an old jar of pot-pourri, with its stiff scented turns of verse and tags of gold embroidery gone tawny in the dust and rust. And in spite of all the old court-stuff about apples and roses and the rest there is a kind of serious twang in it here and there as if the man did care to mean something. I suppose he didn't mind, and liked his life the better on account of her: would have gone on all the same if he had known: fellows do get such fools. I don't think I should have cared much either. Conceive Ernest not liking his wife to talk about it. He found the verses in a book of hers and wanted to burn them: then sat down and read Prodgers on Pantology or something in that way for two hours instead, till Mme de Rochelais called. Clara told me that evening. A treatise on the use of fish-bones as manure I think it was. She will not take the Rochelais view at all, and says Lady Margaret ought to have been hanged or burnt. As for my forefather she calls him about the perfectest knight and fool on record: the sort of man one could have risked being burnt for with pleasure. She would have been a grand châtelaine in the castle days. One would have taken the chances for her sake—rather. And if ever anything were said about her—all such natures do get ill-used—I think and trust you for one would stand by her and speak up for her. She is too good to let the world be very good to her. Tears and brilliant light mixed in her eyes when she talked of that bit of story; the beautifullest pity and anger and passionate compassion. She might have kept Sans reproche on her shield and never written Sans merci on her heart. I believe she could do anything great. She wanted to be at Naples last year; would have outdone Mme Mario in that splendid labour of hers. She says if she were not in mourning already she would put on deeper black for Cavour now; I told her not. If she had been born an Italian and had the chance given her she would have gone into battle as gladly as the best man. That Venice visit last year set the stamp on it. I never saw her so near letting tears really fall as when she quoted that about the "piteous ruinous beauty of all sights in the fair-faced city that death and love fought for when it was alive, and love was beaten; but comes back always to look at the sweet killed body left there adrift between sea and sunset." I am certain Ernest wears her out; this miserable days'-work does tell upon her, and the nerves and head will fail bit by bit if it goes on. Men would trust in her and honour her if she were a man; why cannot women as it is? Whatever comes, she ought to look to us at least; to you and me.

~

21.

Lady Midhurst to Mrs. Radworth.

Ashton Hildred, Sept. 10*th*

I wish my news were of a better sort; but I can only say in answer to your nice kind letter that Amicia is in a very bad way indeed. At least I think so; she has not held up her head for weeks, and her face seems to me changing, as some unusually absurd poet of your generation has observed, "from the lily-leaf to the lily-stem." Stalk he might at least have said, but he wanted a sort of villainous rhyme to "flame." A letter from Reginald the other day put some light and colour into her for a minute, but seemed to leave her worse than ever when the warmth was taken off. Next day she could not come down; I with some conventional brutality forced a way into her room and found her just asleep, her face crushed into the wet pillow, with the moist salt fever of tears on the one cheek upmost—leaden and bluish with crying and watching. I tell her that to weep herself green is no widow's duty, and no sign of ripeness: but she keeps wearing down; is not visibly thinner yet, but must be soon. Her eyelids will get limp and her eyelashes ragged at this rate; she speaks with a sort of hard low choke in the notes of her voice which is perfectly ruinous. Very few things seem to excite her for a second; she can hardly read at all: sits with her chin down and eyes half drawn over like a sleepy sick child. I should not wonder to see her hair beginning to go: she actually looks *sharp:* one might expect her brows and chin to become obtrusive in six months' time. Even the rumour we hear (not at first hand you know) about a Roche-lais *revival* did not seem to rouse or amuse her. If there *is* anything in the chatter, one can only be glad of such an improvement in the second generation; for I cannot well conceive

Frank's marrying, or your approving, a new edition of Mlle Armande de Castigny. Fabien de Rochelais was *the* most victimized, unhappiest specimen of a husband I ever saw: a Prudhomme Coquardeau of good company, if you can take—and will tolerate—the Gavarni metaphor. The life she led him is *unknown;* half her exploits, I believe devoutly, never reached the light— many I suspect never would bear the air. You *must* know what people say of that young M. de Saverny who goes about with them—the man you used to get on so well with two years ago? He *never* turned up during Mme de Saverny's life anywhere—and *months* after the poor wretched lady's death his father produces this child of four, and takes him about as his orphaned heir, and presents him—*notamment* to the Rochelais, who make an infinite ado about the child ever after. Why, at one time, he wanted to marry the girl himself—had played with her in childhood— plighted troth among budding roses—chased butterflies together —Paul et Virginie, nothing less. This was a year ago, just after he went back to France, she being barely out of her convent. Do you want to know why, and how, it was broken up? look in the table of affinities.

Of course, if the girl is nice, tant mieux. Remembering my dear mother, it is not for me to object to a French Lady Cheyne. But a Rochelais—if Rochelais it is to be—you will allow is rather startling. Old M. de Saverny is dead, certainly; which is one safeguard, and really a thing to be thankful for. He was awful: Valfons, Lauzun, Richelieu's own self, hardly more compromising. And here the mother tells. Unluckily, but so it is. Taking one thing with another into account, though, Philomène might get over this well enough. Ce nom tramontain et dévot m'a toujours crispé les nerfs. But if Frank likes her, well and good. People do not always inherit things. Your friend for instance, the amiable Octave, is not very like that exquisite and infamous old father. Only I should be inclined to take time and look well about me. Here again you may be invaluable to the boy. By what I remember I should hardly have thought Philomène de

Rochelais would turn out the sort of girl to attract him. Pretty I have no doubt she is. Octave I always thought unbearable; that complexion of *singed white* always gives me the notion of a sheet of notepaper flung on the fire by mistake and snatched off with the edges charred. Et puis ces yeux de lapin. Et cette voix de serin. The blood is running out, evidently. M. de Saverny père was great in his best days. They used to say last year that Count Sindrakoff had supplanted his ghost auprès de la Rochelais. She is nearly my age, too. But I believe the Russian was a young man of the directory, or thereabouts. I am getting horridly scandalous but Armande was always too much for my poor patience. She thinks herself one of Balzac's women, and gets up affairs to order. Besides, she always fell short of diplomacy through pure natural lack of brain; and yet was always drawing blunt arrows to the head and taking shaky aim at some shifting public bull'seye. I wrote a little thing about her some years since and labelled it "La Femme de Cinquante Ans, Étude;" it got sent to Jules de Versac, who touched it up and put it into the *Timon:* it was the best sketch I ever made. I daresay she knows I wrote it. She avowed to me once her belief that she had a mission to help in reviving, as she said, les grands salons d'*autrefois:* a woman à tête de quenouille, as old Sindrakoff himself once said of her. I should call her head more like a spinning-wheel: perhaps he meant much the same. Her brains are a tangle of ravelled yarn. It amuses me ineffably to find her taking up with Redgie Harewood, I suppose by way of paying indirect court to us. I know he has more than the usual boy's weakness for women twice his own age, but surely there *can* be nothing of that sort here? They seem exquisitely confidential, by his own innocent account. She always did like lamb and veal. The daughter must be too young for him; a woman with natural red and without natural grey is no doubt not yet worth his looking at: that is, unless there were circumstances which made it wrong and unsafe; but I speak of serious things. I thought at one time he was sure to upset all kinds of women with that curious personal beauty of his, as his poor sister used to upset men; he is such a splendid boy to look at, as to face; but now I see his lot in life lies the other way, and he will always be the footstool and spindle of any woman who may choose to have him. Less mischief will come of him that way, which is consoling to remember. Indeed I doubt now if he ever will do any; but if he gets over thirty without some damage to himself I shall be only too thankful. Really I think in default of better I would rather see him than Frank married to Mlle de Rochelais. Lord Cheyne has time and room to beat about in and choose from right or left. Now Redgie, I begin to believe, will have to marry before long. I don't see an atom of fitness in him for the diplomatic service. The sea would have been better, but that (though he never knew it) I prevented when he was a boy by threatening his father with all kinds of obloquy and opprobrious consequences if he let him go. Perhaps even the army might have done. This new Fotherington. crotchet is a pure nuisance. I hate politics without the beard on. I never was in love but once and then it was with Prince Metternich, whom I never set eyes on in my life. A *diplomate* is a dish not worth touching till the crust is thoroughly done; and that crust takes an immense time to bake: and the meat often spoils in the cooking. It would be something too to keep him out of absurdities. We know too well what a head it is when any windmill is set spinning inside it. And without irony, I am convinced Mme de Rochelais must have a real kindly feeling about him. She was out of her depth in love with your father in 1825, when he was still by way of being young: and Redgie now and then reminds me a little of him; Frank is placider, and not quite such a handsome fellow as my brother used to be. It is so like her to come out with old family histories and relics as the best means of astonishing the boy's weak mind; but I did not know she had still any actual and tangible memorials of the time by her. I have been trying to recollect the date of her daughter's birth; she was extant in '46, for I saw her in Paris, a lean child in the *rose blonde* line. Three I should think at the time, or perhaps five: a good ten years younger than Octave de Saverny. Redgie's three or four years over would just tell in the right way: Frank I should call too young. I want you to tell me honestly how you look at it. To me it seems he might brush about the world a little more before he begins marrying. Only this instant come of age, you know. The attachment might be a good thing enough for him. Mlle Philomène I suppose must be clever; there is no reason to presume she can have inherited the poor old vicomte's flaccidity of head and tongue. Very spiritually Catholic, and excitable on general matters, the girl ought to be by this time; Armande I remember was a tremendous legitimist (curious for her) of late years, and has doubtless undertaken to convert Reginald to sane views and weed out his heresies and democracies. I should like to see and hear the process. Since the empire came in I believe she has put lilies on her carpets, and rallied her crew round the old standard with a will. Henri V. must be truly thankful for her. Desloches, the religious journalist, was one of her converts: the man whom Sindrakoff, with hyperborean breadth of speech, once indicated to me as a cochon manqué. Ever since the *Légende des Siècles* came out *I* have called him Sultan Mourad's pig. One might suggest as a motto for his paper that line;

Le pourceau misérable et Dieu se regardèrent.

Edmond Ramel made me a delicious sketch of the subject, with Armande de Rochelais, in sultanic apparel and with a beard beyond all price or praise, flapping the flies off: her victims (social and otherwise) strewing the background. On apercevait en haut, parmi des étoiles, le bon Dieu qui larmoyait, tout en s'essuyant l'œil gauche avec un mouchoir azuré au coin duquel on voyait brodé le chiffre du journal de Desloches, numéro cent. Cette figure béate avait les traits—devinez—du pauvre vieux vicomte Fabien. Je n'ai jamais ri de si bon cœur. Que Victor Hugo me pardonne!

As I suppose nobody thinks just yet of betrothals or such-like, I want to hear what you think of doing for the next month or so.

[122]

It is a pity to leave Lidcombe bare and void all the autumn weeks. The place is splendid then, with a sad and noble sort of beauty in all the corners of it. Such hills and fields, as Redgie neatly expressed himself in that last remarkable lyric of his, "shaken and sounded through by the trumpets of the sea." The Hadleigh sands are worth seeing about the equinox; only heaven knows we have all had sight enough of the sea for one year. Still Frank ought to be about the place now and then, or they will never grow together properly. Why can you not go down together and set up house in quiet sisterly fashion for a little? he has hardly stayed there ten days in all since the spring. After living more than six weeks with you, except that little Lidcombe interlude at the end of July, and those few days in London, it is his turn to play host. Or if any sort of feeling stands in the way of it, why not go to Lord Charnworth's as you did last year? If there is anything sound in the Rochelais business it will grow all the better for a little separation: I am sure I for one would not for worlds mettre des bâtons dans les roues. But if it is a mere bit of intrigue on the mother's part (and I can hardly believe Armande a reliable person) surely it is better cut loose at once, and let drift. I shall try and see Philomène this winter, whether they return or stay. The Charnworths are perfect people and will be only too glad of you all. A cousin's death is no absolute reason for going into a modern Thebaid, nice as he was. And I hardly suppose you still retain your old preference of Octave de Saverny to Lord Charnworth, in the days before the latter poor man married —entirely I have always believed a result of your early cruelty. Now if you stay at home and keep up, in or out of London, the intimacy which seems to be getting renewed, I predict you will have the whole maison Rochelais et Cie upon your hands at Blocksham before you know where to turn. Science will be blown up heaven-high: and Mr. Radworth will commit suicide.

I am getting too terrible in my anticipations, and must come to a halt before all my colours have run to black. Besides our doctor has just left, and the post begins to clamour for its prey. He gives us very singular auguries about his patient. For my own part, I must say I had begun to have a certain dim prevision in the quarter to which he seems to point. At all events it seems she is in no present danger, and we must not press the doubt. I trust you not to intimate the least hope or fear of such a thing happening and only refer to it here to relieve the anxious feeling I might have given you by the tone of my first sentences. It would be unpardonable to excite uneasiness or pity to no purpose. False alarms, especially in the posthumous way, are never things to be excused on any hand. You can just let Frank know that we none of us apprehend any actual risk; which is more than I at least would have said a month since. She is miserably reticent and depressed. I must end now with all loves, as people used to say ages ago. Take good care of them all, and still better care of yourself—on many accounts: and think in the kindest way you can of

Yours most affectionately
H. Midhurst.

~

22.

Captain Harewood to Reginald.

Plessey, Oct. 22nd

My dear Reginald—You will at once begin preparing for your work, unless you wish to throw this chance too over, and incur my still more serious displeasure. That is all the answer I shall make you. You must be very well aware that for years back you have disgracefully disappointed me in every hope and every plan I have formed with regard to you. Of your school and college career I shall have a few words to say presently. It is against my expressed wish and expectation that you are now in London instead of being here under my eye: and even after all past experience of your utter disregard of discipline and duty I cannot but feel surprise at your present proposal. If you do visit the Radworths before returning home, you will do so in direct defiance of my desire. That course, understand, is distinctly forbidden you. After our last interview on the subject I can only consider the very suggestion as an act of an insolent and rebellious nature. I know the construction to which your conduct towards your cousin has not unnaturally exposed you; and you know that I know it. Upon her and upon yourself your inexcusable and puerile behaviour has already drawn down remark and reproach. I am resolved, and I intend that you shall remember I am, to put an end to this. I have come upon a letter from your grandmother, dated some time back—I think before the miserable catastrophe in which you were mixed up at Portsmouth—bearing immediately in every line upon this affair: and I have read it with attention. Secrets of that kind you have no right to have or to keep; and I have every right and reason to investigate them. Another time, if you intend to pursue a furtive line of action, you will do well to make it a more cautious one: the letter I speak of was left actually under my hand, not so much as put away among other papers. Upon the style of Lady Midhurst's address to you I shall not here remark: but you must expect, I should think, to hear that my view of such things is far enough from being the same as hers. Rightly or wrongly, I consider the sort of relation she appears to contemplate in that letter as at once criminal and contemptible: and I cannot pretend to observe it with indifference or toleration. You seem to me to have written and acted childishly indeed, but not the less sinfully. However, I am not now about to preach to you. The One safeguard against natural evil and antidote to natural unwisdom you have long been encouraged to neglect and overlook. All restrictions placed around you by the care of others and of myself you have even thus early chosen to discard. It is poor comfort to reflect that, as far as I know, you have not as yet fallen into the more open and gross vices which many miserable young fools think it almost laudable to indulge in. This can but be at best the working of a providential accident, not the outcome of any real self-denial or Manly self-restraint on your part. Without this I count all fortuitous abstinence from sin worth very little. In a wiser Eye than man's many a seemingly worse character may be purer than yours. From childhood upwards, I must once for all remind you, you have thwarted my wishes and betrayed my trust. Prayer, discipline, confidence, restraint, hourly vigilance, untiring attention, one after another failed to work upon you. Affectionate enough by nature, and with no visibly vicious tendencies, but unstable, luxurious, passionate and indolent, you set at nought all guidance, and never in your life would let the simple noble sense of duty take hold of you. At school you were almost hourly under punishment; at home you were almost daily in disgrace. Pain and disgrace could not keep you right; to disgrace the most frequent, to pain the most severe, you opposed a deadly strength of sloth and tacit vigour of rebellion. So your boyhood passed; I have yet in my ear the remark of one of your tutors—"Severity can do little for the boy, indulgence nothing." What the upshot of your college career was you must remember only too well, and I still hope not without some regret and shame. Absolute inert idleness and wilful vanity, after a long course of violated or neglected discipline in small matters, brought you in time to the dishonourable failure you had been at no pains to avoid.

And yet you know well enough whether or no I have done and purpose even yet to do all for you that I can; whether I have not always been but too ready to palliate and indulge; whether from the very first the utmost tenderest allowance has not been made for you, and the least possible share of your own faults laid to your own charge. This I say you do in your conscience and heart know, and must needs bear me witness to the truth of it. I must confess I have not now much hope left. Little comfort and little pleasure have you ever given me, and I expect to get less from you and less as our lives go on. One thing though I can at worst be sure of; that my own duty shall be done. As long as I can hold them at all, I will not throw the reins upon your neck. I will not, while I can help it, allow you to speak, to act, if possible to think, in a way likely to injure others. I desire you not to go to the house of a man whom I know you profess, out of your own inordinate impertinence and folly, to dislike and contemn: I trust you at least as a gentleman to respect my opinion and my confidence, if I cannot count on your obedience as my son; on these grounds I do believe and expect you will not visit Blocksham. Mr. Ernest Radworth is a man infinitely your superior in every way. For many years now he has led a most pure, laborious, and earnest life. The truly great and genuine talents accorded to him at his birth he has submitted to the most conscientious culture and turned to the utmost possible advantage. To himself he has been consistently and admirably true; to others I believe he has invariably been most helpful, beneficent, exemplary in all his dealings. By one simple process of life he has kept himself clean and made all near him happy. From first to last he was the stay and the pride of his family; and since he has been left alone in his father's place he has nobly kept up the distinction which in earliest youth and even boyhood he very deservedly acquired. A fit colleague and a fit successor, this one (as you would acknowledge if you were capable of seeing), for the greatest labourers in the field of English science. Excellent and admirable in all things, he is in none more worthy of respect than in his private and domestic relations. There is not a man living for whom I entertain a more heartfelt regard—I had wellnigh said reverence—than for Mr. Radworth. I verily believe he has not a thing, humanly speaking, to be ashamed of in looking back upon his past life. Every hour, so to say, has had its share of noble toil—and therefore also its share of immediate reward. For these men work for the world's sake, not for their own: and from the world, not from themselves, they do in time receive their full wages. There is no more unsullied and unselfish glory on earth than that of the faithful and reverent scientific workman: and to such one can always reasonably hope that the one thing which may perhaps be wanting will in due time get supplied. The contempt or disrelish of a young, idle, far from noteworthy man for such a character as that of Ernest Radworth is simply a ludicrous and deplorable phenomenon. You are incompetent to appreciate for one moment even a tenth part of his excellence. But I am resolved you shall make no unworthy use of a friendship you are incapable of deserving. Of your cousin I will here say only that I trust she may in time learn fully to apprehend the value of such a heart and such a mind. By no other path than this of repentant and retrospective humility can she ever hope to attain real happiness or honour. I should, for Ernest's sake, truly regret being compelled to adopt Lady Midhurst's sufficiently apparent opinion that she is not worthy to perceive and decide on such a path.

You now know my desire; and I do not choose to add any

further appeal. Expecting for the sake at least of your own immediate prospects, that you will follow it, I remain

Your anxious and affectionate father

Philip Harewood.

~

.

23.

Francis Cheyne to Mrs. Radworth.

Lidcombe, Nov. 18*th*

I have just read your letter. Come by all means next month, and stay as long as you can. Every day spent here by myself is a heavier and more subtle irritation to me than the one before. Reginald will come, for a few days at least; his foreign outlook seems to have fallen back into vapour and remote chance. The captain was over here lately, looking pinched and hard: a head to make children recoil and wince at the sight of it. He is still of great help to me. As to Mme de Rochelais, to be quite open, I had rather not meet her just now: so you will not look for me before the day they leave you. Afterwards I may perhaps come over to escort you and Ernest, if it turns out worth while. Anything to get about a little, without going out of reach. News I suppose must come from Ashton Hildred before very long. At such a time I have no heart to spare for thinking over plans or people. Your praise of Mlle de Rochelais is of course all right and just. She is a very jolly sort of girl, and sufficiently handsome: and if Redgie does marry her I shall just stop short of envying him. Does madame really want me to take such a gift at her hand? Well and good; it is incomparably obliging; but then when I am looking at Mlle Philomène and letting myself go to the sound of her voice like a song to the tune, unhappily there gets up between us such an invincible exquisite memory of a face ten times more beautiful and loveable to have in sight of one; pale when I saw it last, as if pulled down by its hair, heavily weighted about the eyes with a presage of tears, sealed with sorrow and piteous with an infinite unaccomplished desire. The old deep gold hair and luminous gray-green eyes shot through with colours of sea-water in sunlight and threaded with faint keen lines of fire and light about the pupil, beat for me the blue-black of Mlle de Rochelais. Then that mouth of hers and the shadow made almost on her chin by the underlip—such sad perfect lips, full of tender power and faith, and her wonderful way of lifting and dropping her face imperceptibly, flower-fashion, when she begins or leaves off speaking; I shall never hear such a voice in the world, either. I cannot and need not now pretend to dissemble or soften down what I feel about her. I do love her with all my heart and might. And now that, after happy years, she is fallen miserable and ill, dangerously ill for aught I know and incurably miserable,—who can say?—it is not possible for me sitting here in her house that I have had to drive her out of, to think very much of anything else, or to think at all of any other woman in the way of liking. This is mere bare truth, not sentiment or excited fancy by any means, and you will not take it for such a sort of thing. If I can never marry the one woman perfectly pleasant to me and faultlessly fit for me in the whole beautiful nature of her, I will never insult her and my own heart by marrying at all. Aunt Midhurst's view of the Rochelais family has no great weight with me; but I have a little hope now, after reading what she says to you, that as she is clearly set against the chance of any other marriage for me she may perhaps be some day brought to think of the one desire of my whole life as a possible thing to fulfil. Even to you I dare not well hint at such a hope as that; but you must now understand for good how things are with me: if not that, then nothing. You take her reference to Redgie Harewood to be a feint, and meant spitefully. I think not; she has the passions of intrigue and man-agement still strong; likes nothing so well evidently as the sense of power to make and break matches, build schemes and overset them. I should like to see Harewood married, and peace again at Plessey; he is not a bad fellow; and she was always fond of him. I will say he earned that at Portsmouth, but I hate to hear of his being able to write to her now, and then see and think how much there is between us to get over. If I could get at her by any way possible I could keep her up still: but I can hardly see how he is to help her much. Then again if he were to marry they might see each other; and in no end of ways it would be a good thing for him. His idolatry is becoming a bore, if not worse; you should find him an ideal to draw his worship off you a little. I know so well now how miserable it is to feel on a sudden the thing turn serious and have to fight it before one has time to see how. If it were fair to tell you all I have had to remember and regret only since this year began, and only because I know how after Cheyne's death her gentle goodness would make her wretched at the thought of past discontent with him—and heaven knows she could not but have felt him less than she was; and perfect she was to him always. I wish now we had never played at feelings. For she did not love me and never could. Even if she were not perfect, and if both had been free to love or not love, I should not have had a decent chance. What I could do to make up for the lamentable adorable self-reproach I was fool enough to cause her feeling! I wish people would blame her to me and let me fight them. I can't fight *her* for blaming herself. I write the awfullest stuff, because I am really past writing at all. If I could fall to work and forget, leave off thinking for good, turn brute, it would be only rational for me. I who have helped to hurt her, and would have set myself against the world to spare her, what do you conceive she thinks of me? This air that has nothing of her left it chafes me to breathe. I know how sometimes somewhere she remembers and misses things that she had got used to, little chance things that were about her in her husband's time. A book or two of hers were left; you will see them sent when you come; I cannot write, and cannot send them without a word. I am more thoroughly afraid of hearing from Lady M. again than I ever was of anything on earth: no child could dread any torture as I do that. It is quite clear you know that they expect a confinement—in some months' time perhaps. God knows I wish there had been a son. Only they will not say it, so I must stay here and take my trouble. It does not startle me; nothing can well be worse for me

[132]

or better than it is now. There is no such pleasure to be had out of my name or house that I need want to fight for it or hold to it. I do hope they will make things good to her. You need hardly express anger about the poor aunt. Those two are her children, and she always rather hated us for their sakes. Indeed as about Reginald I am not sure she is so far out of the way. You must see that Ernest flinches now and then when he is talked of: and without any fear of scandal one may want to avoid the look of it. He is not the sort of fellow to be sure of; not that he is a bad sort. Enfin (as she says) you know what it means: Ernest is not great in the way of company, and Redgie and you are just good friends; the woman is not really fool enough to think evil, though she is rather of the vulturine order as to beak and diet. For the rest, I know how wise and kind you are: it is a shame to lean on you as I do, but you are safe to come to.

~

24.

Lady Cheyne to Mrs. Radworth.

Ashton Hildred, Nov. 22*nd*

My dear Clara—I have got leave to write and thank you. Nothing has made me so happy for a long time as to know how kind you have been and that you are still such good friends with me. It was no want of thankfulness to you that made me leave Portsmouth in that horrid way to get home here. I knew how good you had been, and you are not to make me out too bad. To hear from you, even such a little word, was nicer than to get the things you sent. But I was as glad as I could be to have some of them back. I would never have let any one send for them to Lidcombe, so it was all the kinder of you to do it in this way. I hope you will all be well there, and quite happy while you stay. It is nice to think of people about the poor house. They are all bent on making me out ill. I am not ill in the least, only faint now and then, and always very tired. I am terribly tired now all my life through, awake and asleep. I feel as if there was nothing nice to think of in the world, and as if it were easier to begin crying than thinking. It is only because I am foolish naturally and afraid to face things. If people were less good to me I should be just as afraid to feel at all, or at least to say I did. But good as they are now, my own nearest friends here could not have been better to me than I *know* you were *then*—writing letters and nursing and saving me all sorts of wretched things. You were as good as Reginald; and I had only you two to help me through but you did all that could be done, both of you, and I knew you did. When I am most tired and would like to *let go* of everything else, I try and hold on to my remembrance of that. If I had not been a little worthy to be pitied, I hope now and then you would not have been quite so good.

I am sorrier than I can say to hear how foolish you think him. Ever since that, I have thought of you two together. You say it so kindly too, that it is wretched to hear said. I do hope it is only his silly candid habit of shewing things he feels and thinks: he always thought about you so much and in such an excited way. You are so much beyond me, and except us two he never had any close ally among his own relations; there are hardly any other women you know. If I had been like you it would have been different: but so few people will take him at his best, poor boy, and I am so little use, though he is fond of me.

I had got a sort of hint from my grandmother which broke the surprise of the news you send me. I hope, as you seem to wish for it, that Mlle de Rochelais and your brother may have all things turn out as they would like; and I shall be as happy as possible to know they do. It is not the least a painful hearing to me that there will be a wedding at the right time. I am only too glad there should be some one there, and I am sure if you both are so fond of her she must be perfectly nice. Tell me when to congratulate. I wish I had ever seen her: nobody here knows at all what she is like. But I seem to have heard people say her mother was not pretty.

They will not let me write any more: my pen is to be dragged off if I try. And really there is this much reason in it, that I am most stupidly tired, and see myself opposite too hideous to speak of. I feel running down; but I don't mean to run out for some time yet. So don't let there be any one put out on such a foolish account as that. I hope Mr. Radworth's head and eyes keep better; they are of rather more value than mine, and I am always sorry to hear of his going back in health. My love to Redgie, and try to make him good.

~

25.

Reginald Harewood to Edward Audley.

Lidcombe, Dec. 15*th*

I am not coming out at all. I can't now; the whole concern is
blown up. I have had a most awful row with my father; you know
the sort of way he always does write and talk; and two months ago
he gave me the most incredible blowing-up—I suppose no fellow
ever got such a letter. So I just dropped into him by return of
post, and let the thing lie over. He chose to pitch into her too, in
the most offensive way. Now I'm not going to behave like a sneak
to her because she is too good for them. She trusts me in the most
beautiful way. I would give up the whole earth for her: Frank
would have made an end of that fellow long ago if he had the right
sort of pluck. And you see a man can't let himself be bullied into
skulking. It's all fair chaffing about it if you please, but you don't
in the least know what the real thing is like. Here she is tied down
and obliged to let that sort of animal talk to her and go about with
her and take her by the hand or arm—I tell you I have seen it. It
was like seeing a stone thrown at her. And she speaks to him
without wincing. I do think the courage of women is something
unknown. I should run twenty times a day if I couldn't fight. He
brings her specimens of things. You can't conceive what a voice
and face and manner the fellow has. She lets him talk about his
symptoms. He tells me he wishes he could eat what I can. It
would be all very well if he had anything great about him. I
suppose women can put up with men that have: but a mere
ingenious laborious pedant and prig, and a fellow that has hardly
human ways, imagine worshipping that! I believe he is a clever
sort of half-breed between ape and beaver. But the sort of thing
cannot go on. I found her yesterday by herself in the library here,

looking out references for him. The man was by way of being ill upstairs. She spoke to me with such a sad laugh in her eyes, not smiling: and her brows winced, as they never do for him whatever he says. She is so gentle and perfect when he is there: and I feel like getting mad. Well, somehow I let her see I knew what an infernal shame it was; and she said wives were meant for the work. Then I began and told her she had no sort of right to take it in that way, and she couldn't expect any fellow to stand and look on while such things were—and I would as soon have looked on at Haynau, any day. I daresay I talked no end of folly, but I was regularly off my head. Unless she throws me over I never will give her up. She never will let her brother know how things are with her. But to see him sit by her ought to be enough for a man with eyes and a heart. I know you were a good deal in love last year, but Miss Charnworth couldn't have put anybody into such a tender fever of pity as this one puts me; you can't be sorry for her; and I don't think you can absolutely worship anything you are not a little sorry for. To have to pity what is such a way above you—no one could stand that. It gives one the wish to be hurt for her. I think I should let him insult me and strike me if she wanted it. Nothing hurts me now but the look of her. She has sweet heavy eyes like an angel's in some great strange pain; eyes without fear or fault in them, which look over coming tears that never come. There is a sort of look about her lips and under the eyelids as if some sorrow had pressed there with his finger out of love for her beauty and left the mark. I believe she knew I wanted her to come away. If there were only somewhere to take her to and hide her and let her live her own way out of all their sight and reach, that would do for me. I tell you, she took my hands sadly into hers and never said a word, but looked sideways at the floor, and gave a little beginning kind of sigh twice: and I got mad. I don't know how I prayed to her to come then. But she turned on me with her face trembling and shining, and eyes that looked wet without crying, and made me stop. Then she took the books and went out, and up to him. Do you imagine I can be off and on or play tricks with my love for such a woman as that? because of my father perhaps, or Ernest Radworth? She has a throat like pearl-colour, with flower-colour over that; and a smell of blossom and honey in her hair. No one on earth is so infinitely good as she is. Her fingers leave a taste of violets on the lips. She is greater in her mind and spirit than men with great names. When she talks of noble things one can see something thicken and throb at the side of her neck. Only she never lets her greatness of heart out in words. I don't think now that her eyes are hazel. She has in her the royal scornful secret of a great silence. Her hair and eyelashes change colour in the sun. I shall never come to know all she thinks of. I believe she is doing good somewhere with her thoughts. She is a great angel, and has charge of souls. She has clear thick eyebrows that grow well down, coming full upon the upper lid, with no gap such as there is above some women's eyes before you come to the brow. They have an inexplicable beauty of meaning in them, and the shape of the arch of them looks tender. She has charge of me for one. I must have been a beast or a fool if there had not been such a face as that in the world. She has the texture and colour of rose-leaves crushed deep into the palms of her hands. She can forgive and understand and be angry at the right time: things that women never can do. You know Lady Midhurst is set dead against her, and full of the most infernal prejudice. The best of them are cruel and dull about each other. I let out at her (Ly M. that is) one day when we spoke of it, and she stopped me. "She is always very good to you," she said; which is true enough. "You and your sister are her children, and she always rather hated Frank and me for your sakes. I like her none the worse, for my part. I don't know that she is so far wrong about you. Once I could have wanted her to like me, but we must put up with people's deficiencies. It is very unreasonable of course, but she does not like me in the least, I quite know:" and the way she smiled over this no one could understand without knowing her. "Only there is

[138]

one thing to be sorry about; that hard pointed way of handling things leaves her with the habit of laughter that shrinks up the heart she has by inches." Those words stuck to me. "If she believed or felt more than she does, her cleverness and kindness would work so much better. As it is, one can never go to her for warmth or rest; and one cannot live on the sharp points of phrases. She has edges in her eyes and thorns in her words. That perpetual sardonic patience which sits remarking on right and wrong with cold folded hands and equable observant eyes, half contemptuous in an artistic way of those who choose either—that cruel tolerance and unmerciful compassion for good and bad—that long tacit inspection as of a dilettante cynic bidden report critically on the creatures in the world—that custom of choosing her point of view where she can see the hard side of things glitter and the hard side of characters refract light in her eyes, till she comes (if one durst say so) to patronize God by dint of despising men—oh, it gets horrid after a time. It takes the heart out of all great work. Her world would stifle the Garibaldis. It is all dust and sand, jewels and iron, dead metal and stone and dry sunshine: like some fearful rich no-man's-land. I could as soon read the *Chartreuse* as listen to her talk long; it is Stendhal diluted and transmuted: and I never could read cynicism." You see how her thoughts get hold of one; I was reminded of her first words and the whole thing came back on me. She said just that; I know the turn of her eyes and head as she spoke, and how her cheeks and neck quivered here and there. Then she made all excuses, the gentlest wise allowances; you see what a mind and spirit she has. She keeps always splendid and right. She can understand unkindness to herself you see, never dreaming that nothing can be so unnatural as that; but not a dry ignoble tone of heart and narrow hardness of eye. Not to love greatness and abhor baseness, each for its own sake—that is the sort of thing she finds unforgiveable and incomprehensible. She would make all things that are not evil, and have not to be gone right at and fought with till they give in, brave and just, full of the beauty of goodness and a noble liberty: all men fit men to honour and all women fit women to adore.

That is what she is. Only if I were to write for ever and find you in heavy reading for centuries I should never get to express a thing about her. Fancy any one talking of that little Rochelais girl. *She* does, and to me; or did till I made her see it was no use, and I didn't like it as chaff. Philomène is a good pretty child, and as to heart and mind, believes in Pius-Iscariot and the vermin run to earth this year at Gaeta. They think my father might put up with that. He used to admire the men of December till they did something to frighten the ruminant British bull at his fodder, and set that sweet animal lowing and thrusting out volunteer bayonets by way of horns in brute self-defence. I remember well how he spoke once of the Beauharnais to me, apropos of my reading the *Châtiments* one vacation. It was before you went down I think that we had a motion up about that pickpocket. My father believes in the society that was saved; he holds tight to the salvation-by-damnation theory. "A strong man and born master"—all that style of thing, you know. Liberty means cheese to one's bread, then honey, then turtle-fat—*Connu.* "La patrie, c'est un bifteck aux pommes." Libre à vous, MM. les doctrinaires! What infinite idiocy and supreme imbecility to get hanged, burnt, crucified for one's cause! You want proof you are a fool? you are beaten: all's said. The smell of the martyrdom is the refutation of the martyr—in the nostrils of a pig. And when people have ideas like that and act on them, how can one expect them to see the simplest things rightly? how should they know a great spirit or noble intellect from a base little one? Souls don't carry badges for such people to know them by: and whatever does not walk in uniform or livery they *cannot* take into account. As to me, and I suppose all men who are not spoilt or fallen stolid are much the same, when I see a great goodness I know it—when I meet my betters I want to worship them at once, and I can always tell when any one is born my better. When I fall in with a nature and power above me I cannot help going down before it. I do like admiring; service of one's masters must be good for one, it is so perfectly pleasant. Then too one can never go wrong on this tack. I feel my betters in my blood; they send a heat and sting all through one at first sight. And the delight of feeling small and giving in when one does get sight of them is beyond words: it seems to me all the same whether they beat one in wisdom and great gifts and power, or in having been splendid soldiers or great exiles, or just in being beautiful. It is just as reasonable to worship one sort as the other; they are all one's betters, and were made for one to come down on one's knees to, clearly enough. Victor Hugo or Miss Cherbury the actress, Tennyson or a fellow who rode in the Balaklava charge when you and I were in the fifth form, we must knock under and be thankful for having them over our heads somewhere in the world; and small thanks to us. But when men who are by no means our betters won't do so much as this, and want to walk into us for doing it, I don't see at all that one is bound to stand that. So that if I am ever to be turned out of my way, it won't be by anything my father may say or do.

I suspect you repent of writing and reading by this time; but please remember how you did go into me last year about Eleanor; and you know by this time there was not so much even for a fellow in love to say about her.

Yours always,

R. E. Harewood.

~

26.

Lady Cheyne to Reginald Harewood.

Ashton Hildred, Jan. 14ᵗʰ 1862

My dearest Reginald—I am writing to-day instead of our grand-mother. She is very unwell and wants you to hear from us. They will not let her trouble or exert herself in any way, but she is bent on your getting a word: so as I am well enough to write I must take her place. I am afraid she is upset on your account. I think she has even exchanged letters with your father about it. They seem to fear something very bad for you. You know by this time how much we both love you, and ought to care a little for us. I know I must not talk now as if I could fall back on self-esteem or self-reliance. I don't the least want to appeal in that style, but just to plead with you as well as I may. I am stupid enough too, and can't put things well. Only, except the people here at home, you are the one person left me that I may let myself love. I am very grateful to you, and I beg you to let me come in this way to you. You must see there is nobody now that I love as well. I want you to remember as I do how good you were once. If I am ill it comes of miserable thought. You talk of her compassionate noble na-ture. Dearest, if she has any mercy, let her shew it and save you. It is cruel to make people play with poison in this way. I would not blame her for worlds, I want to thank her and keep good friends, but she must not let you run to ruin. Think what imaginable good end can there be to this? I suppose she is infinitely clever and brave as you say, but how can she face things *for you?* Every one would say the horridest things. Do you want shame for her? It would break your life up at the beginning. I have no right to accuse—should have none anyhow—but one has always a right to be sorry. I see you could not be happy even if all were given up on both sides. Don't let her give all up. I daresay she might: and that of course is braver than any treason. If you knew my own great misery. Sometimes I feel the whole air hot about me; I should like to cry and moan out loud, or beat myself. I am not old, and if I live all my time out I shall never feel as if my face had a natural look; I shall suspect people, and be afraid of my shame. I cannot take it bravely. For you know, when my husband was alive I did not love him. I wish I were very old, and gone foolish. I was false in every word and thought I had. I cannot kill myself you see, even by writing it down. Thinking of it only hurts, without doing harm: I want to be done harm to. I never spoke to you at Portsmouth. If you never did know, you see now. I thought you all knew. I seemed to myself to have the eyes of a woman who has been cheating and lying to some one just dead. I was penitent enough to have had the mark on me. It would be better than playing false, to leave her husband. But then she takes you, your life and all. I do think she must not be let. I hate repeating what was said viciously; and God knows I must not talk or think scandal: but Mme de Rochelais, her own friend and yours, says things about her and M. de Saverny; it is no unkindness of my grandmother's. She does not like Clara now, but she is clear of all that, quite. And there were letters, certainly. Mme de R. said so; they were the cleverest she ever saw; but not good to write. It was two or three years ago. M. de Saverny let her see them. It was base and wretched; and he keeps them. He is a detestable man; but you cannot get over that. I believe no harm of her. Only you will not let her take you from us. You must see it would be the end of all our pleasure and hope. People would laugh too. Mme de Rochelais says, Elle a toujours voulu faire sauter les gens en marionnettes; mais mon Dieu, quel saut de carpe que celui-ci! Quant à ce pauvre Octave, il s'est déjà cassé quelque ressort à vouloir faire paillasse auprès d'elle. C'est une femme qui s'amuse le plus innocemment du monde à tenir baraque d'amourettes,—en tout bien tout honneur, cela s'entend. These are her *own words:* I saw her letter about you. If you want to *stand by her* as you say, how can you begin by helping people to scandal? I am so sorry for you, I know you are too fond of her and good to her and would never give her up; and I am not fit to help. Still, whatever I am, I do know there must be right and wrong somehow in the world. You should not make so much misery. I don't mean as to the people nearest you both. On your side of course I cannot tell you how to look at things: and as to hers I can only be sorry, *and am very.* But you know after all my mother is something to you while she lives: you are my very own brother and dearest one friend. I wish you might see her. She is so full of the tenderest beautiful ways, so made up of sweet things and small faultless loves that never fail one. I know what she hears hurts her. She shews little, but she cried when our grandmother gave her letters to read. You might be so good to us, for we can never do anything or be much to you. If evil comes of this I shall think we were all born to it. There will be *no one* left to think of or speak to without some afterthought or aftertaste of memory and shame. The names nearest ours will have stings in them to make us wince. It is not good for us to try and face the world. It has beaten all that ever took heart to stand up against it. Surely there is something just and good in it, whatever we think or say, let it look ever so unfair and press ever so hard. I write this as well as I can, but it is very hard to write. I cannot make way any further: my head and hand and eyes ache, and the sight of the words written down makes me feel sick; the letters seem to get in at my eyes and burn behind them. You must be good and bear with my letter. With all our loves I remain

Your affectionate Sister
A. C.

~

27.

Reginald Harewood to Mrs. Radworth.

(London) Jan. 19th

I will wait for you till your own time; only, my dearest, I will not have you wait out of pity or fear. All that is done with: my time is here, with me; I have the day by the hand, and hold it by the hair. We have counted all and found nothing better than love. I do just hope there may be something for me to give up or go without; I see nothing yet. You are so far too much better to me than all I ever knew of. I sit and make your face out between the words, and stop writing to look. You ought to have given me that broken little turquoise thing you used to have hung to your watch. I wonder all men who ever saw you do not come to get you away from me—fight me for you at least. For I shall never let you out of my hands when I have you well in them. If one had seen you and let you slip! I knew I should get you some day or die. Because I was never the least worth it. Because you need not have been so good, when you were so beautiful that nothing you did could set you off. But you know I loved you ages first. When I was a boy and got sight of you, I knew stupidly somehow you were the best thing there was. You were very perfect as a child; I know the clear look of your temples under the hair; and the fresh delicious tender girl's hair drawn off and made a crown with. I want to know what one was to have done without that? I don't think you cared about me a year ago—not the least, my love that is now. I had to play Palomydes to your Iseult a good bit; but are you ever going to be afraid of the old king in Cornwall after this? as if we were not any one's match, and anything we please. Tu seras dame, et moi comte, Puisque nous nous aimerons. You shall scent me out the music to that some day; the song made of the sound of

[145]

flowers and colour of music: you ought to know the notes that go
to the other version of it. We shall have such a love in our life
that all the ends of it will be sweet. You will not care too much
about the people that could be no use to you. Could a brother
save you when you wanted saving? Besides I have hold of you.
The whole world has no claim or right in it any longer to set
against mine. Let those come that want you and see if I let go of
you for any man. There will not be an inch of time, not a corner
of our life without some delicious thing in it. Let them tell us
what we are to have instead if we give each other up. I shall get to
be worth something to you in time. You say now you never found
anything yet that had the likeness of your mate. I have much
more of you than all the earth could deserve; I should like to see
myself jealous of old fancies in a dead dream. That poor child at
A. H. writes me piteous little letters in the silliest helpless way
about the wrong of this and the right of that; she has been set
upon and stung by some poisonous tale-bearing or other; she
wants one to forbear loving for others' sake, and absolutely cites
her own poor terrified little repentance after her husband's death
on remembering some unborn-baby-ghost of a flirtation which
she never *told,* some innocuous preference which sticks to the
childish little recollection like a sort of remorse. It is pitiable
enough, but too laughable as well: for on the strength of it she
falls at once to quoting vicious phrases and transcribing mere
batlike infamies and stupidities of the owl-eyed prurient sort, the
base bitter talk of women without even such a soul as serves for
salt to the carrion of their mind. We know where such prompt-
ings start from. What is it to me, if I am to be the man fit to match
with you by the right of my delight in you, that you have tried to
find help or love before we came together, and failed of it? Let
them shew me letters to disprove that I love you, and I will read
them. Till they do that, I mean to hold to you, and make you hold
to me. I thought there had been more in her than one sees: but
she has a pliable soft sort of mind not unlike her over-tender

cased-up exotic kind of beauty. I don't want women to carry the sign-mark of them all over, even to the hair. Hers always looks sensitive hair, and has changes of colour in it. A woman should keep to the deep sweet dark with such a noble silence of colour in the depth of it, rich reserved hair with a shadow and a sense of its own, that wants no gilt setting of sunbeams to throw out the secret beauty in it. I should like to see yours painted; that would beat the best of them. Promise I shall have sight of it again soon. I want you as a beggar wants bread to eat; I have the sort of desire after your face that wounded men must have after water. I wish there were some mark of you carved on me that I might look at. Now this is come to me I wonder all day long at all the world. Nobody else has this; but they live in a sort of way. I do think at times that last year my poor little plaything of a sister and your brother were almost ready to believe they knew what it was—as you hear children say. They had the look and behaviour of a girl and boy playing themselves into belief in their play. And all the while we have drawn the lot and can turn the prize over, toss and catch it in our hands. All little loves are such poor food to keep alive on: our great desire and delight, infinite faith and truth and pleasure, will last our lives out without running short. You know who says there are only three things any lover has to say; Je t'aime; aime-moi; merci. I say the last over for ever when I fall to writing. I thank you always with all my heart and might, my darling, for being so perfect to me. We will go to France. There will be money. Write me word when you will. And I love you. We will have a good fight with the world if it comes in our way. Let us have the courage of our love, knowing it for the best thing there is. There is so little after all has been thought of, either to brave or to resign. I shall make you wear your hair the way we like. Your sort of walk and motion and way of sitting has just made me think of the doves at Venice settling in the square, as we shall see them before summer. There is a head like you in San Zanipolo; a portrait head in the right corner of a picture of the

Virgin Crowned: we shall see that. Only it has thick curled gold hair, like my sister's. You had that hair when you sat to Carpaccio; you have had time to grow perfecter in since. I can smell the sweetness of the sea when I think of our journey. I like signing my name now it has to do with you. My name is a chattel of yours, and yours a treasure of mine. Let it be before spring; and love me as well as you can.

Reginald Edw. Harewood.

~

28.

Lady Midhurst to Mrs. Radworth.

Ashton Hildred, Jan. 30*th*

My dear Clara—I have not yet made up my mind whether or no
you will be taken at unawares by the news I have to send you.
You must make up yours to accept it with fortitude. Amy has just
enriched the nation and impoverished your brother by the
production of a child—male. In spite of her long depression and
illness it is a very sufficient infant, admirable in all their eyes
here. Frank I am sure expected to hear of this in time. While
there was any doubt as to the child's (I mean Amy's and should
say the mother's) state of health, we could not resolve on pub-
lishing the prospect of her confinement. I may all but say it was a
game of counter chances. That it has come to no bad end you will
I am sure be as glad as we are. Eight months of mourning were
enough to make one thoroughly anxious. The boy does us as
much credit as anything so fat and foolish, so red and ridiculous,
as a new baby in good health can do. I suppose we shall be
inundated with troubles because of this totally idiotic fragment of
flesh and fluff which my daughter has the front and face to assert
resembles its father's family: such is the instant fruit of sudden
promotion to grandmotherhood. And I am a great-grandmother;
and not sixty-two till the month after next. Armande will never
allow me my rank as junior again: yet I recollect her grown-up
patronage of your father and me when we were barely past school
age, and she barely out: la dame aux belles cousines I called her,
and him le petit Jean de—what is it?—Saintré? I suppose my
son-in-law will be guardian. I do hope nobody will feel upset at
this: our dear Frank is too good a knight to grudge the baby its
birth. Poor little soft animal, one could wish for all our sakes

some of its belongings off the small shoulder of it; but as it has chosen to come they must stick to it. Amy is in a noticeable flutter of impatience to get the christening of it well over; she has high views of the matter, picked up of late in some religious quarter. Edmund-Reginald we mean to have it made into, and I must have Redgie Harewood come and vow things for it; he will make an admirable surety for another boy's behaviour; and the name will do very well to be washed under. Unless indeed Frank would be chivalrous enough to halve the charge: then we might bracket his name with the poor father's. Don't ask him if you think he would rather keep off; we don't want felicitation, only forgiveness; that we must have. If I had not been tricked, and caught in the springe of a sudden promise to take the weighty spiritual office on myself, I should implore you to be godmother. As it is I suppose the sins and the sermons must all come under my care. Break the news as softly as you can; there must always be something abrupt, questionable, vexatious in a business of the sort. It is hard to have to oust one's friends and shift one's points of view at a week's notice. However, here the child is, and we must set about the management of it. I shall make Frederick undertake the main work at once as guardian and grandfather. He writes to Lidcombe by this post. Amy is already better than she has been for months, and very little pulled down in spite of a complete surprise. She makes a delicious double to her baby, lying in a tumbled tortuous nest or net of hair with golden linings, with tired relieved eyes and a face that flashes and subsides every five minutes with a weary pleasure; she glitters and undulates at every sight of the child as if it were the sun and she water in the light of it. You see how lyrical one may become at an age when one's grandchildren have babies. I should have thought her the kind of woman to cry a fair amount of tears at such a time, but happily she refrains from that ceremonial diversion. She is the image of that quivering rest which follows on long impassive trouble and the labour of days without deeds: quiet, full of life, eager and at ease. I imagine she has no memory or feeling left her from the days that were before yesterday. She and the baby were born at one birth, and know each as much as the other of the people and things that went on before that.

Get your husband to take a human view of the matter—I suppose his ideas of a baby which is neither zoophyte nor fossil are rather of the vaporous and twilight order of thought—and bring him down for the christianizing part of the show, if he will condescend so far. He could take a note or two on the process of animal development by stages, and the decidedly misty origin of that comic species to which our fat present sample of fleshly goods may belong. About Reginald; I may as well now say once for all that I think I can promise to relieve you for good of any annoyance in that quarter. We must both of us by this time be really glad of any excuse to knock his folly about you on the head. Here is my plan of action, to be played out if necessary; if you have a better, please let me know of it in time, before I shuffle and deal; you see I show you my hand in the most perfectly frank way. That dear good Armande, who really has an exquisite comprehension of us all and our small difficulties, has got (heaven I *hope* knows how, but I need hardly say I don't) a set of old letters out of the hands of the sémillant and seductive M. de Saverny fils, and put them into mine, where you cannot doubt they are in much better keeping. Octave is not exactly the typical braggart, but there is a dash in him of that fearful man in *Madame Bovary*—the first lover I mean; varnished of course and well kept down, but the little grain of that base nature does leaven and flavour the whole man. He will never have, never so much as understand, the splendid courtesy and noble reticence of a past age. His father had twice his pretensions and less than half his pretension; and so it will be with all the race. Knowing as you do now that the papers exist, you must feel reasonably glad to be well out of his hands. Not of course, my dear niece, that I could for one second conceive you have what people would call any reason to be glad of such a thing, or that I would in the remotest way insinuate there was ever so much as a seeming indiscretion on one side. But when you permitted Octave to open up on that tack you were not old or stupid enough to see, what duller eyes could hardly have missed of, the use your innocence might be put to: a thing, to me, touching and terrible to think of. Cleverness, like goodness, makes the young less quick to apprehend wrong or anticipate misconstruction than stupid old people are. In this case my heavy-headed experience might have been a match for your rapid bright sense. I have hardly looked at your correspondance; had not other eyes been there before mine, nothing of course would induce me to look now; but I know Mme de Rochelais well enough to be sure she has not skipped a word. I must look over my hand, you see, as it is. It was hard enough to get them from her at all, as you may imagine; I hardly know myself how I did get it done; mais on a ses moyens. What I have seen, in the mean-time, is quite enough to shew me that one of these letters would fall like a flake of thawed ice on the most feverish of a boy's rhapsodies. With the least of these small ink-and-paper pills I will undertake to clear your suitor's head at once, and bring him to a sane and sound view of actual things. I know what boys want. They will bear with any imaginable antecedent except one which makes their own grand passion look like a pale late proof taken off at a second or third impression. All the proofs before letters you left in Octave's hands long ago: your sentiment (excuse, but this *is* the way he will take it) has come down now to the common print. Shew him what the old friend really was to you, and he will congeal at once. I don't imagine you ever meant actually to let him thaw and distil into a tender dew of fine feeling at your feet; you would no doubt always have checked him in time—if he would always have let you. But then upon the whole it is as well to have a weapon at hand. I believe he has grown all but frantic of late and has wild notions of the future: amusing to you no doubt while they last, but not good to allow of. Now I should not like to lay the Saverny letters before him and refrigerate his ideas by that process; one had rather dispense with it while one can; but sooner than let his derangement grow to confirmed mania and

[152]

become the practical ruin of him, I must use my medicines. I know, after he had taken them, he would be sensible again, and give up his dream of laws broken and lives united. Still I had rather suppress and swamp altogether the Saverny-Rochelais episode and all that hangs on to it: rather escape being mixed up in the matter at all, if I can. There is a better way, supposing you like to take it. Something you will see must be done; suppose you do this. Write a quiet word to Reginald, in a way to put an end to all this folly for good. Say he must leave off writing; we know (thanks to your own excellent feeling and sense) that he does write. Lay it on your husband if you like: but make it credible. Leave no room for appeal. Put it in this way, suppose, as you could do far better than I can for you. That an intimacy cannot last which cannot exist without exciting unpleasant unfriendly remark. That you have no right, no reason, and no wish to be offered up in the Iphigenia manner for the sake of arousing the adverse winds of rumour and scandal to the amusement of a matronly public. That you are sorry to désillusionner even "a fool of his folly," and regret any vexation you may give, but do not admit (I would just intimate this much, as I am sure you can so well afford to do) that he ever had reason for his unreason. That in a word, for your sake and his and other people's, you must pass for the present from intimates to strangers, and may hope if both please to lapse again in course of time from strangers into friends. I think this will do for the ground-plan: add any intimation or decoration you like, I for one will never find or indicate a fault. Only be unanswerable, leave no chance of room for resistance or reply, shut him up as you say at once on any plea, and I will accept your point of action and act after it: he need never and never shall be made wiser on the subject than you please. The old letters shall never have another chance of air or light. If you don't like writing to silence him I can but use them faute de mieux: for of course the boy *must* be brought up short; but I think my way is the better and more graceful. Do not you?

It is a pity that in putting a stop to folly we must make an end

[153]

of pleasant intercourse and the friendly daily habits of intimate acquaintance. I can quite imagine and appreciate the sort of regret with which one resigns oneself to any such rupture. For my part it is simply the canon of our church about men's grandmothers which keeps me safe on Platonic terms with our friend. Some day I shall console and revenge myself by writing a novel fit to beat M. Feydeau out of the field on that tender topic. I suppose Ninon never attained such an honour. Figure to yourself the exquisite effects that might so well be made. The grandmother might at last see my hero's ardour cooling after a bright brief interval of birdlike pleasure and butterfly love—volupté suprême et touchante où les rides se fondent sous les baisers et les lois s'effacent sous les larmes—all that style; and when compelled to unclasp her too tender arms from the neck of her jeune premier, the venerable lady might sadly and resignedly pass him on, shall we suppose to his aunt? a pathetic intrigue might be worked out by which she would (without loving him) seduce her son-in-law so as to leave the coast clear for the grandson who had forsaken her, and with a heart wrung to the core by self-devoted love, prepare her daughter's mind to accept a nephew's homage: finally see the young people made happy in each other and an assenting uncle, and take arsenic; or, at sight of her work completed, die of a cerebral congestion (one could make more *surgery* out of that) invoking on the heads of child and grandchild a supreme benediction baptized in the sacred tears which drop on the grave of her own love. Upon my word I think it an idea which might bear splendid fruit in the hands of a great realistic novelist: I see my natural profession now, but I fear too late.

In good earnest I am sorry this must be the end. A year ago I was too glad to enlist your kindness on Reginald's behalf; and I can see how that kindness led you in time to put up with his folly. I am sure I can but feel the more tenderly and thankfully towards you if indeed you have ever come to regret for a moment that things were as they are. I have no right to reproach, and no heart; no one has the right; no one should have the heart. You know my

[154]

lifelong abhorrence of the rampant Briton, female or male; and my perfect disbelief in the peculiar virtue of the English hearth and home. There is no safeguard against the natural sense of liking. But the time to count up and pay down comes for us all; we have no pleasures of our own; we hold no comforts but on sufferance. Things are constant only to division and decline. The quiet end of a friendship I have at times thought sadder than the stormiest end of a love-match. Chi sa? but I do know which I had rather keep by me while I can. It is a pity you two poor children are not to be given more play, or to see much more of each other. He will miss his friend, her sense and grace and wit, the exquisite companionship of her, when he has done with the fooleries of sentiment. You, I must rather hope for his sake, may miss the sight of him for a time, the ardent ways and eager faiths and fancies, all the freshness and colour and fervour of his time and temperament; perhaps even a little the face and eyes and hair; ce sont là des choses qui ne gâtent jamais rien; we never know *when* we begin or cease to care for such things. I too have had everything handsome about me, and I have had losses. You see, my dear, the flowers (and weeds) will grow over all this in good time. One thing and one time we may be quite sure of seeing; the day when we shall have well forgotten everything. It is not uncomfortable as one gets old to recollect that we shall not always remember. The years will do without us; and we are not fit to keep the counsel of the fates. In good time we shall be out of the way of things, and have nothing in all the world to desire or deplore. When recollection makes us sorry, we can remember that we shall forget. I never did much harm, or good perhaps, in my life; so at least I think and hope; but I should be sorry to suppose I had to live for ever in sight of the memory of it. Few could rationally like to face that likelihood if they once realized it. There is no fear; for a time is sure to come which will have to take no care of the best of us, as our time has to take none of plenty who were better. I shewed you, now some eighteen months since, when it first appeared I think, that most charming song of *Love and Age,* the one bit of verse that I have liked well enough for years to dream even of crying over; the sweetest noblest piece of simple sense and manly music, to my poor thinking, that this age of turbulent metrical machinery has ever turned out; and it, by the by, hardly belongs to you. Your people have not the secret of such clear pure language, such plain pellucid words and justice of feeling. Since my first reading of it, the cadences that open and close it come back perpetually into my ears like the wash of water on shingle up and down when I think of times gone or coming. I never coveted a verse till I had read that in *Gryll Grange:* there is in it such an exquisite absence of the wrong thing and presence of the right thing throughout: just enough word for the thought, and just enough thought for the matter: a wise, sweet, strong piece of work. We shall leave the years to come nothing much better than that. What is said there about love and time and all the rest of it is the essence incomparably well distilled of all that we can reasonably want or mean to say. We must let things pass; when their time is come for going, or when if they stay they can but turn to poison, we must help them to be gone. And then we had best forget.

It is a dull empty end; a blank upshot; but you know what good authority we have for saying that there are no such things as catastrophes. I admit it is rather a case of girl's head and fish's tail: but you must see how deep and acute that eye of Balzac's was for such things. His broad maxims are the firmest-footed and least likely to slip of any great thinker's I know; they have such tough root and tight hold on facts. As to our year's work and wages, we may all say truly enough; Le dénouement c'est qu'il n'y a pas de dénouement. I prophesied that last year, when there first seemed to be a likelihood of some domestic romance getting under way. The point of such things, as I told Amy, is just that they come to nothing. There were very pretty scandalous materials; the making of an excellent roman de mœurs—intime et tant soit peu scabreux. Amy and your brother, you doubtless remember, gave symptoms of being touched, as flirting warmed to feeling; they had begun playing the game of cousins with an over-liberal allowance of sentiment. Redgie again was mad to upset conventions and vindicate his right of worshipping you; had no idea for his part of keeping on the sunny side of elopement. Joli ménage! one might have said at first sight—knowing this much, and *not* knowing what Englishwomen are here well known to be. And here we are at the last chapter with no harm done us yet. You end as model wife, she as model mother; you wind up your part with a suitor to dismiss, she hers with a baby to bring up. All is just as it was, as far as we all go; the one difference, lamentable enough as it is, between this and last year is the simple doing of chance, and quite outside of any doing of ours. But for poor Edmund's accidental death, which I am fatalist enough to presume must have happened anyhow, we should all be just where we were. Not an event in the whole course of things; not I think so much as an incident; very meagre stuff for a French workman to be satisfied with. We must be content never to make a story, and may instead reflect with pride what a far better thing it is to live in the light of English feeling and under the rule of English habit.

You will give Frank my best love and excuses in the name of us all. He must write to me before too long. For yourself, please accept this as I mean it; act as you like or think wise, and believe me at all times

Your most affectionate aunt
Helena Midhurst.

~

29.

Francis Cheyne to Lady Midhurst.

Lidcombe, Feb. 15*th*

My dear Aunt Helena—I shall be clear of this place to-morrow; I am going for a fortnight or so to Blocksham. I quite agree it will be best for me not to have the pleasure of seeing Amicia. You will I hope tell her how thoroughly and truly glad I am; and that if I could have known earlier how things were to turn out it would have simply saved me some unpleasant time. As to meeting, when it can be pleasant to her, I shall be very grateful for leave to come: and till then it is quite good enough to hear of her doing well again. Only one thing could add to my perfectly sincere pleasure at this change—to know I had been able to bring it about of my own will and deed; as I would have done long since. I hope she will get all right again and the sooner for being back here. I shall not pretend to suppose you don't know now that I care more about her and what happens to her than about most things in the world. If all goes well with her nothing will go far wrong with me while I live. I daresay I shall do well enough for the professions yet when I fall to and try a turn with them; and I cannot say, honestly, how thankful I am to be well rid of a name and place that I never could have been glad of.

We have more to thank you for than your kindness as to this. I have seen my sister since you wrote, and she has shown me some part of your letter. I do not think we shall have any more trouble at home. My brother-in-law knows nothing of it. She has written I believe to Reginald; I must say she was angry enough, but insists on no notice. If she were ever to find home all but too comfortless to put up with I could not well wonder; she has little there to look to or lean upon. We are out of the fighting times, but if M. de Saverny or any other man living were to try and make base use of her kindness and innocence, I suppose no one could well blame or laugh at me if I exacted atonement from him. As it is I declare if he comes in her way, and I find he has not kept entire silence as to the letters written when she was too young and too good to dream what baseness and stupidity there is among people, I will prevent him from going about and holding up his head again as a man of honour. Any one from this time forth who gives her any trouble by writing or by word of mouth shall at once answer to me for it. I have no right to say that I believe or do not believe she has never felt a regret or a wish. She is answerable to no man for that. I do say she has given nobody reason to think of her or a right to speak of her except with all honour: and if necessary I wish people to know I intend to stand by what I say.

She is quite content, and I believe determined, to see no more of R. H. for some time; quite ready too to allow that accident and a time of trouble let him perhaps too much into the secret of an uncongenial household life, and that she was over ready to look for companionship where it was hardly wise to look for it. Few men (as she says) at his age could have had the sense or chivalrous feeling to understand all and presume upon nothing. She said it simply, but in a way to make any one ashamed of mistaking for an instant such a quiet noble nature as she has. I have only now to thank you for helping us both to get quit of the matter without trouble or dispute. I should be ashamed to thank you for doing my sister the simple justice not to misconstrue her share in it. If there ever was any evilspeaking I hope and suppose it is now broken up for good. For the rest, I have agreed to leave it at present in your hands and hers: but if ever she wants help or defence I shall of course be on the outlook to give it. I have only to add messages from us both, and remain, my dear aunt,

Your affectionate nephew
Fr. Cheyne.

~

30.

Lady Midhurst to Lady Cheyne.

My dear Child—First salute the fellow-baby in my name, and then you shall have news. I assume that is done, and will begin. Two days here with your father have put me up to the work there is to do. I shall not take you into counsel as to estate affairs, madame la baronne. When the heir is come to ripe boyhood you may take things in hand for yourself. Meantime we shall keep you both in tutelage and grow fat on privy peculation; so that if you find no holes in the big Lidcombe cheese when you come to cut it, it will not be the fault of our teeth. So much for you and your bald imp; but you want news I suppose of friends. I called at Blocksham and saw the Radworths in the flesh—that is in the bones and cosmetics; for the male is gone to bone and the female to paint. The poor man calls aloud for an embalmer: the poor woman cries pitifully for an enameller. They get on well enough again by this time, I believe. To use her own style, she is *dead beat,* and quite safe; viciously resigned. I think we may look for peace. She would have me racked if she could no doubt, but received me smiling from the tips of the teeth outwards, and with a soft dry pressure of the fingers. Not a hint of anything kept back. Evidently too she holds her brother well in leash. Frank pleased me: he was courteous, quiet, without any sort of affectation dissembled or displayed. I gave him sufficient accounts, and he was grateful; could not have taken the position and played a rather hard part more gracefully than he did. We said little and came away with all good speed. The house is a grievous sort of place now, and likely to stay so. I have no doubt she will set all her wits to work and punish him for her failure. She will hardly get up a serious affair again, or it might be a charity to throw her some small animal by way of lighter food. It would not surprise me if she fell to philanthropic labour, or took some devotional drug by way of stimulant. The *baraque d'amourettes* is a bankrupt concern, you see: her sensation-shop is closed for good. I prophesy she will turn a decent worrying wife of the simpler Anglican breed; home-keeping, sharp-edged, earnestly petty and drily energetic. Negro-worship now, or foreign missions, will be about her mark; perhaps too a dash and sprinkle of religious feeling with the chill just off: with a mild pinch of the old Platonic mixture now and then to flavour and leaven her dead lump of life: I can imagine her stages well enough for the next dozen or score of years. Pity she had not more stock in hand to start with.

I have been at Plessey too; one could not be content with seeing half a result. Captain H. was more gracious to me than you would believe. I suspect the man has wit enough to see that but for my poor offices his boy would be now off heaven knows whither, and stuck up to the ears in such a mess as nothing could ever have scraped him thoroughly clean of. He and Redgie are at last on the terms of an armed peace; very explosive terms you know, but decent while they last, and preferable to a tooth-and-nail system. I will say I behaved admirably to him: asked what plans he had for our boy—what he thought the right way to take with him—assented and consented and suggested and submitted; altogether made myself a model. It is a fact that at this day he thinks Redgie might yet be in time bent and twisted and melted down into the Church mould of man—cut close to the fit of a surplice. Now I truly respect and enjoy a finished sample of clergy; no trade makes better company; they make a cross between artist and diplomate which is charming. Then they have always about them a sort of suppressed sense of something behind—some hint of professional reserve which does not really change them, but does colour them; something which fails of being a check on their style, but is exquisitely serviceable as a sauce to it. A cleric who is also a man of this world and has

[161]

nothing of the crossbone type is as perfect company as you can get or want. But conceive Redgie at any imaginably remote date coming up recast in that state out of the crucible of time! I kept a bland face though, and hardly sighed a soft semi-dissent. At least I said we might turn him to something good yet; that I did hope and think. The fatherly nerve was touched; he warmed to me expressively. I am sure now the poor man thought he had been too hard on me all these years in his private mind, put bitter constructions on very innocent conduct of mine—had something after all to atone for on his side. He grew quite softly confidential and responsive before our talk was out. Ah, my dear, if you could see what odd tumbled shapeless recollections it brought up to find myself friendly with him and exchanging wishes and hopes of mine against his, in all sympathy and reliance! I have not earned a stranger sensation for years. Ages ago, before any of your set were born; before he married your mother: when he was quite young, poor, excitable, stupid, and pleasant; infinite ages ago, when the century and I were in our thirties and he in his twenties, we used to talk in that way. I felt ready to turn and look round for things I had missed since I was six years old. I should hardly have been taken aback if my brothers had come in and we had set to playing together like babies. To be face to face with such a dead and buried bit of life as that was so quaint that stranger things even would have fallen flat after it. However there was no hoisting of sentimental colours on either side: though I suppose no story ever had a stranger end to it than ours. To this day I don't know why I made him, or let him, marry your mother.

I told him I must see Redgie and take him in hand by private word of mouth. He was quite nice about it, and left the boy to me, smiling even as he turned us over to each other; more benign than he ever was when I came over to see Redgie in his school-days: a time that seemed farther off now than the years before his birth. I can't tell you how odd it was to be thrown back into '52 without warning—worse than the proverbial middle of next week. I will say for Redgie he was duly ashamed, and never

[162]

looked sillier in his boyish time than when I took him to task. Clara, I told him, had as far as I knew behaved excellently; but I wanted to have facts. Dismissal was legible on him all over: but the how I was bent on making out. So in time I got to some fair guess at the manner of her final stroke. It was sharp and direct. She wrote, not exactly after my dictation (which I never thought she need do, or would), but simply in the resolute sacrificial style. She forbade him to answer; refused to read him, or reply if she read; would never see him till all had blown over for good. It seems she could not well deny that not long since he might have carried her off her feet—which feet she had now happily regained. Heaven knows, my dear child, what she could or could not deny if she chose: I confess I cannot yet make up my mind whether or no she ever had an idea of decamping, and divorcing with *all* ties: it is not like her; but who can be sure? She has none now. Honestly, I do suspect that a personal bias of liking did *at times* get mixed up with her sentimental spirit of intrigue: and that she would have done things for Redgie which a fellow ten years older or a thought less handsome would never have made her think of: in effect, that she was in love with him. She is quite capable of being upset by simple beauty: if ever she were to have a real lover now I believe he would be a fool and very nice-featured. It is the supreme Platonic retribution; the Nemesis of sentimental talent, which always clutches such runners as she is before they turn the post. There was a small grain of not dubious pathos in her letter: she was fond enough of him to regret what she did not quite care to fight for. What she told him I don't know, nor how she put it: I can guess though. She has done for his first love, at any rate. He knows he was a fool and I did not press for his opinion of her. One may suppose she put him upon honour and made the best of herself. I should guess too that she gave hints of what he might do in the way of annoyance if he were not ready to forgive and make friends at a distance. That you see would prick him on the chivalrous side, and he would obey and hold his tongue and hand at once—as he has done. Anyhow the

[163]

thing is well killed and put underground, with no fear of grave-stealers; there is not even bone enough left of it to serve the purpose of a moral dissection. The chief mourner (if he did but know it) should be Ernest Radworth. I could cry over that wretchedest of husbands and students when I think of the thorns in his pillow, halters in his pew and ratsbane in his porridge, which a constant wife will now have to spend her time in getting ready.

Redgie was very fair about her: would have no abuse and no explanation. "You see" he said "she tells me what she chooses to tell, and that one is bound to take, but I have no sort of business now to begin peeping and snuffing at anything beyond. I thought once you know we both had a right to ask or answer: that was when she seemed to care about it. One can't be such a blackguard as to try and take it out of her for changing her mind. She was quite right to think twice and do as she chose; and the least I can do now is to keep off and not get in her way." Of course the boy talks as if the old tender terms between them had been broken off for centuries, and their eyes were now meeting across a bottomless pit of change. I shall not say another word in the matter: all is as straight and right as it need be: though *I know* that only last month he was writing her the most insane letters. These one may hope she will think fit to burn. To him I believe she had the sense never to write at any length or to any purpose but twice, this last time being one. And so our little bit of comedy slips off the stage without noise and the curtain laps down over it. Lucky it never turned to the tearful style as it once threatened to do.

I need not say that Redgie does not expect to love seriously again. Not that he says it; he has just enough sense of humour to keep the assertion down; but evidently he thinks it. Some one has put a notion into the captain's head about Philomène de Roche-lais—Clara herself perhaps, for aught I know; she is quite inge-nious enough to have tried that touch while the real play was still in rehearsal. Nothing will come of that though; I shall simply reconquer the boy, and hold him in hand till I find a woman fit to have charge of him. I hope he will turn to some good, seriously. Some of his friends are not bad friends for him: I like that young Audley well enough, and he seems to believe in Redgie at a quite irrational rate. Perhaps I do too. He must take his way, or make it; and we shall see.

As to the marriage matter, I have thought lately that Armande might be given her own way and Frank married to the girl—if they are all of one mind about it. It sounds rather Louis Quinze to bâcler a match in this fashion, but I don't see why it should not come to good. He may as well marry now as later. I don't at all know what he will make in the professional line; and he can hardly throw over all thoughts of it. I did think of proposing he should be at the head of the estates for a time in the capacity of chief manager and overlooker; but there were rubs in the way of that plan. It is a nice post and might be made a nice sinecure—or demi-cure with efficient business people under and about one; not bad work for a cadet de famille, and has been taken on like terms before now. We owe him something; however, we may look for time to pay it. I will confess to you that if the child had been a girl I meant to have brought you together at some future day. You must forgive me: for the heir's marrying the dowager would have made our friends open their eyes and lips a little: and things are much better as they are.

~

Explicit.

Textual Notes

The textual notes that follow contain a selection from the hundreds of cancellations by Swinburne in his MS. and revisions by him in the later versions of the text. I have not recorded mere errors introduced by others, which Swinburne inadvertently passed in seeing his work through the press. The notes are of two sorts: 1) readings in angle brackets, followed by the notation MS., show parts that were crossed out by Swinburne as he was writing the manuscript on which this text is based; 2) readings of this text, followed by readings from the later texts, with the appropriate signs, show Swinburne's subsequent alterations: for example, *om.* 77, 05 means that the reading was deleted by Swinburne for *The Tatler* in 1877, and that it is omitted from the Chatto and Windus edition of 1905. The authority for the changes recorded here, unless otherwise noted, is established by Swinburne's own corrections in the transcript from which the *Tatler* text was printed, and in the proof sheets for the 1905 edition. (The transcript also contains John Nichol's suggested alterations, referred to in a few of the following notes.) The exceptions are those places where pages from the transcript and the proofs are lacking. In the transcript these are: *from* p. 14, l. 8 points about . . . *to* p. 14, l. 22 . . . Lady Midhurst; *from* p. 33, l. 7 in her. . . . *to* p. 43, l. 15 . . . game depends; *from* p. 60, l. 28 at all. . . . *to* p. 61, l. 27 . . . at once; *from* p. 119, l. 10 turned up . . . *to* p. 127, l. 31 . . . possible advantage; *from* p. 140, l. 13 thrusting out . . . *to* p. 145 *opening of letter 27; from* p. 165, l. 14 head of the . . . *to the end of the text.* In the proofs there is a break *from* p. 17, l. 25 points of childish . . . *to* p. 29 *the beginning of Part V of the Prologue.*

[*Title*] *lacking from Swinburne's MS. but present in the transcript and in* 77; Love's Cross-Currents A Year's Letters 05.

[*Dedication*] *Swinburne's MS. has no dedication but the transcript has* To My Husband *om.* 77; 05 *has a new dedication:*

TO THEODORE WATTS-DUNTON

As it has pleased you to disinter this buried bantling of your friend's literary youth, and to find it worth resurrection, I must inscribe it to you as the person responsible for its revival. Were it not that a friend's judgment may always seem liable to be coloured by the unconscious influence of friendship, I should be reassured as to its deserts by the approval of a master from whose verdict on a stranger's attempt in the creative art of fiction there could be no reasonable appeal—and who, I feel bound to acknowledge with gratitude and satisfaction, has honoured it by the sponsorial suggestion of a new and a happier name. As it is, I can only hope that you may not be for once mistaken in your favourable opinion of a study thrown into the old epistolary form which even the giant genius of Balzac could not restore to the favour it enjoyed in the days of Richardson and of Laclos. However that may be, I am content to know that you agree with me in thinking that in the world of literary creation there is a legitimate place for that apparent compromise between a story and a play by which the alternate agents and patients of the tale are made to express what befalls them by word of mouth or of pen. I do not forget that the king of men to whose hand we owe the glorious history of Redgauntlet began it in epistolary form, and changed the fashion of his tale to direct and forthright narrative when the story became too strong for him, and would no longer be confined within the limits of conceivable correspondence: but his was in its ultimate upshot a historic and heroic story. And I have always regretted that we have but one specimen of the uncompleted series of letters out of which an earlier novel, the admirable Fortunes of Nigel, had grown up into immortality. The single sample which Lockhart saw fit to vouchsafe us is so great a masterpiece of dramatic humour and living imagination that the remainder of a fragment which might well suffice for the fame of any lesser man ought surely to have been long since made public. We could not dispense with the doubtless more generally amusing and interesting narrative which superseded it: but the true and thankful and understanding lover of Scott must and will readily allow or affirm that there are signs of even rarer and finer genius in the cancelled fragment of the rejected study. But these are perhaps too high and serious matters to be touched upon in a note of acknowledgment prefixed to so early an attempt in the great art of fiction or creation that it would never have revisited the light or rather the twilight of publicity under honest and legitimate auspices, if it had not found in you a sponsor and a friend.

Pages 3–4: *To the Author.*] *om*. 05 *(entire letter deleted)*.

Page 8, l. 22–page 9, l. 2: "What," . . . critic.] *om*. 77, 05.

Page 9, l. 8: Reform, ⟨ temperance ⟩] MS.

Page 9, ll. 19–20: woman. Decidedly . . . it was.] woman. Had fate or date allowed it,—but stern chronology forbade,—he would assuredly have figured as president, as member, or at least as correspondent of the Society for the Suppression of Anatomy, the Society for the Suppression of Sex, or the Ladies' Society for the Propagation of Contagious Disease (Unlimited). But these remarkable associations, with all their potential benefits to be conferred on purblind and perverse humanity, were as yet unprofitably dormant in the sluggish womb of time. Nevertheless the house decidedly might have been livelier than it was. 77, 05.

Page 9, ll. 26–30: he had . . . humaines."] and 77, 05.

Page 9, l. 33: as . . . she-socialist] *om.* 77, 05.

Page 11, l. 4: the last] a past 05.

Page 11, l. 7: Captain ⟨ Geo. ⟩ Harewood] MS.

Page 11, l. 8: 183⟨ 9 ⟩] MS.

Page 12, ll. 3–4: and . . . again.] *om.* 77, 05.

Page 12, ll. 14–15: Ask . . . woman.] *om.* 05.

Page 12, l. 16: (and is)] *om.* 05.

Page 12, ll. 24–25: has been] had been 05.

Page 12, l. 33–page 13, l. 5: For . . . resolute.] *om.* 05.

Page 12, l. 34: religion; ⟨ at the frosty touch of satire or indifference, the tender pigeon shudders up into a mere quivering frost-bitten heap of feathers, the merest parody of a tremulous dove; ⟩ but] MS.

Page 13, l. 28: of ⟨ her cousin's ⟩ company] MS.

Page 15, l. 26: which we forbear from giving] from history and tradition 77, 05.

Page 15, l. 32: did not ⟨ his mother's son ⟩] MS.

Page 20, l. 31: ⟨ Eleven ⟩ Nine] MS.

[169]

Page 22, ll. 27–29: There were bits . . . half an hour.] *om.* 77, 05.

Page 22, l. 30: It's . . . a whole swarm] It's just like a swarm 77, 05.

Page 22, l. 31: Makes . . . bone.] *om.* 77, 05.

Page 22, l. 33: six] three 77, 05.

Page 22, l. 34–page 23, l. 3: Pepperbottom . . . for short.] *om. (Nichol suggested this deletion)* 77, 05.

Page 23, l. 7: day] week 77, 05.

Page 23, l. 9: the whole school] my division 77, 05.

Page 23, l. 28–page 24, l. 15: Well, young one . . . with a dreadful unction.] And Reginald proceeded to recite certain episodes, apocryphal or canonical, from the life of a lower boy; giving the details with a dreadful unction. *(Nichol had suggested that Swinburne delete the whole passage from page 23, l. 12 (I don't think . . .) to page 24, l. 14)* 77, 05.

Page 24, ll. 19–20: or the clear . . . flesh,] *om. (Nichol suggested this deletion)* 77, 05.

Page 24, ll. 20–21: His eyes . . . syllables.] *om. (Nichol suggested this deletion)* 77, 05.

Page 24, l. 30: feasted on his flesh] *left standing by Swinburne in spite of Nichol's suggestion to delete these words.*

Page 25, l. 30: yesterday . . . rubbed. Riding] yesterday. It was a jolly good rod, and quite fresh, with no end of buds on; but you see you can't understand. Of course you can't. Then you see there was the ride over here. Riding 77, 05.

Page 25, l. 34–page 26, l. 25: Frank had begun . . . desire.] *Nichol suggested that Swinburne delete this passage; at first he did, but then wrote "Stet" in the margin and kept it.*

Page 26, l. 2: by God] by Jove 77, 05.

Page 26, ll. 5–6: to look sharp and kneel down] to go down 77, 05.

Page 26, ll. 13–14: between each] at every other 77, 05.

Page 26, ll. 20–22: absolutely stung the youthful hearer . . . made his blood shiver] made the youthful hearer's blood shiver 77, 05.

Page 26, ll. 23–25: It had roused . . . desire.] *om.* 77, 05.

Page 26, ll. 29–35: In . . . satisfied.] *om.* 05.

Page 27, l. 10: thirty-⟨nine⟩] MS.

Page 27, l. 20: a man ⟨ten or⟩ twelve or ⟨perhaps almost twenty⟩] MS.

Page 28, l. 34: he allowed ⟨, only character⟩] MS.

Page 29, l. 24: ⟨2*nd* of⟩ May] MS.

Page 29, l. 29: 1855] 1857 77, 05.

Page 31, l. 2: of. ⟨I am old enough to have seen what is the upshot of small family fashion fights.⟩] MS.

Page 34, l. 12: the ⟨poor young man⟩] MS.

Page 34, l. 13: they ⟨had⟩ both ⟨been drinking⟩] MS.

Page 34, l. 14: up ⟨after they had had their wine⟩] MS.

Page 38, l. 3: French novel] French *portière* 77, 05.

Page 38, l. 3: a ⟨monthly⟩ nurse ⟨—Feydeau plus Gamp⟩] MS.

Page 40, date: ⟨April 3*rd*⟩] MS.

Page 40, l. 15: Graves] Greaves 05 *passim.*

Page 40, l. 18: Nanine] Marie 77; Hélène 05.

Page 41, l. 14: beaten about] sermonized 05.

Page 43, l. 20: stupide⟨st⟩ of my ⟨three⟩ brothers] MS.

Page 44, l. 25–page 46, l. 30: Did you ever hear of old Mr. Chetwood . . . ought to manage.] *om.* 05.

Page 45, l. 5: ⟨Ch⟩aulnes] MS. *passim.*

Page 45, l. 5: Beaulnes] B*** 77 *passim.*

Page 45, l. 30: a Mme de Montreuil she was,] *om.* 77.

Page 46, l. 14: On parle encore] *om.* 77.

Page 46, ll. 15–16: de certain plat découpé à la duchesse de Beaulnes] *om.* 77.

Page 46, l. 21: ugliest ⟨housemaid⟩ name] MS.

Page 46, ll. 23–25: Mr. Chetwood . . . over.] *om.* 77.

Page 46, l. 29: de Montreuil] de M*** 77.

Page 46, l. 30: Be *light*] But I want you to be *light* 05.

Page 48, date: Jan. ⟨19⟩] MS.

Page 48, l. 1: in ⟨three days'⟩ time] MS.

Page 51, l. 1: everybody ⟨(including his obedient and unfortunate sister)⟩] MS.

Page 51, ll. 6–7: such ⟨an⟩ insignificant ⟨matter⟩ as ⟨my own wedding⟩.] MS.

Page 52, l. 3: schoolmaster] tutor 05.

Page 52, ll. 13–15: As to the looks . . . my head.] *om.* 05.

Page 53, l. 24: Dr. ⟨—Birchley was it or was that his nickname? I forget⟩] MS.

Page 54, ll. 30–31: When she was ⟨ sixteen ⟩] MS.

Page 56, ll. 12–13: six months. ⟨ Next year old Lord Cheyne ⟩ died, and ⟨ three ⟩ year⟨ s ⟩ after that] MS.

Page 59, heading: Ed⟨ mund ⟩ Audley] MS. *passim*.

Page 59, opening: ⟨ If you can wait three days over your time I mean to meet you in Paris by the middle of the month. Fortunately the paternal doors remain barred and the paternal hands open, so that I receive my small income without having to inflict myself on ce cher homme. That old woman is without exception the jolliest old lady in this earth; she managed splendidly for me. You see when I do write to you you must make your mind up to pass from the praises of my cousin to the praises of my grandmother; I am a person of strong family feelings, you will observe. I am so full just now of these domesticities that I must pour myself out in some direction; you come in the way of my confidences, tant pis; prepare yourself for a letter of the most sentimental. ⟩] MS.

Page 59, l. 13: Hadle⟨ y ⟩] MS. *passim*.

Page 60, l. 11: the captain] the pater 05.

Page 65, l. 18: Alfred W⟨ ellwoo ⟩d] MS. *passim*.

Page 66, l. 5: for ⟨ a man belonging to either of the other classes ⟩] MS.

Page 68, l. 14: Rigolboche] *(*Note*)

Où est la très sage Heloïs?
* * * *
Mais où sont les neiges d'antan!
(ED., 1877.)

Swinburne added this footnote for 77 *but dropped it in* 05 *and replaced* that Rigolboche of a Muse *with* that rampant young Muse.

Page 68, l. 15: (don't repeat my similies, please)] *om.* 05.

Page 69, l. 8: recandescence] *Swinburne's MS. is uncertain—the reading could be* recrudescence *but the transcript and the editions have* recandescence *and in the 1905 proofs Swinburne rejected a reader's query to change to* recrudescence.

[173]

Page 69, ll. 17–24: Mr. C. . . . men and things.] *om.* 05.

Page 71, ll. 1–2: (You will admit . . . I abstained.)] *om.* 05.

Page 78, date: April 20*th*] *Thomson wrote* 28*th* *which Swinburne kept in* 77, 05.

Page 78, l. 8: changing. ⟨If I wanted to bolt I should have been off long since.⟩] MS.

Page 78, l. 9: because ⟨my poor dear old dry bagfull of sciences is not a green tree (your style)⟩] MS.

Page 83, ll. 15–18: I can remember . . . he would, too.] *om.* 05.

Page 89, ll. 26–27: care for ⟨the politics of 1900.⟩] MS.

Page 92, l. 26: boy ⟨misses his womankind much, or⟩] MS.

Page 94, opening lines: ⟨I put myself in your power once for all, trusting to your mercy. I entreat you not to compel me to what I still hope to avoid. Do not write again⟩] MS.

Page 94, l. 2: any of us ⟨, or if you repent in the least,⟩] MS.

Page 94, l. 22: was ⟨so treacherous and infamous⟩ at heart I could not have ⟨endured the sight of her face.⟩] MS.

Page 94, l. 26: tired. ⟨If I knew you were to be in the next house⟩ ⟨close at hand to-morrow⟩ Or go] MS.

Page 95, l. 6: kept right, ⟨—not quite to lose all claim to honour or⟩] MS.

Page 95, l. 9: sorry. ⟨For I love you⟩ It is too late] MS.

Page 95, l. 11: God ⟨meant us to be so⟩] MS.

Page 96, footnotes 1 and 2: *om.* 05.

Page 97, footnote 1: *om.* 77, 05 *(omitted by Thomson from his transcript and not restored by Swinburne).*

Page 100, ll. 2–3: Mind . . . n'épanchez pas.] *om.* 05.

Page 105, l. 9: help the heart.] "help the heart"—wise phrase of a wiser poet than your brother ever will make. 77, 05.

Page 106, date: 20*th*] 28*th* *(Thomson had written* 18*th* *which Swinburne changed to* 28*th*) 77, 05.

Page 109, date: Ju⟨ne⟩] MS.

Page 109, date: July 26*th*] Aug. 16*th* 77, 05.

Page 109, l. 4: thief⟨. The house puts me off; the woods will have none of me: the old garden beds are put out at me⟩] MS.

Page 111, date: ⟨July 21*st*⟩] MS.

Page 111, l. 7: over ⟨. Some of E.'s things are to be sent you through my father.⟩] MS.

Page 111, l. 12: Arthur ⟨Darrell⟩] MS.

Page 111, l. 16: once ⟨about some breakfast of⟩] MS.

Page 112, l. 1: Rochelais] Rochelaurier 77, 05 *passim.*

Page 112, l. 16: two-thirds] one-third 77, 05.

Page 112, ll. 18–25: C'est un jeune démon . . . really good.] *om.* 05.

Page 113, l. 7–8: the ⟨Wardour⟩ ⟨Carew⟩ Herbert Society] MS.

Page 116, ll. 4–7: Ce sang . . . rien qui vaille,] *om.* 05.

Page 117, l. 17: sunset." ⟨—quoting that song of Avisam's⟩] MS.

Page 118, date: ⟨Aug⟩] MS.

Page 120, ll. 7–8: Count S⟨u⟩drakoff] MS. *passim.*

[175]

Page 120, l. 17: ⟨ Paul de Vers ⟩] MS.

Page 120, ll. 19–24: She avowed . . . ravelled yarn.] *om.* 05.

Page 121, ll. 10–21: I don't see . . . in the cooking.] *om.* 05.

Page 123, l. 12: than ⟨ a month ⟩] MS.

Page 125, date: ⟨ Sept. 2*nd* ⟩] MS.

Page 126, l. 30: almost hourly] incessantly 05.

Page 126, l. 31: almost daily] constantly 05.

Page 127, l. 7: avoid ⟨ ; and at the end of last autumn I had the pleasure of reflecting, as I looked back over my son's school and college days, on three memorable features in them, of which his friends could justly boast; that he had got himself constantly flogged, twice plucked, and once rusticated. The distinction was noble and well merited; any boy and any father might be proud of it for life. ⟩] MS.

Page 130, date: ⟨ Sept. ⟩ ⟨ Oct. ⟩] MS.

Page 130, l. 1: ⟨ My dear Sister ⟩ I have] MS.

Page 130, l. 1: next ⟨ week ⟩] MS.

Page 132, l. 7: how. ⟨ If we had not played at confidences there would never have been ⟩] MS.

Page 132, l. 13: always ⟨ ; except some such feeling, she never had a thing to blame herself for, as you and we all know: and when I think my senseless intrusion of sympathy and impertinence of affection may have given her cause to regret a word now and then said to me about him, I could kill myself for shame. ⟩] MS.

Page 132, ll. 13–18: I wish now . . . her feeling!] *om.* 05.

Page 132, l. 31: that. ⟨ Write me a word soon, please, and say nothing about Reginald or Philomène or any one else you can help. I know how wise and kind you are. It is a shame to rest on you as I do: but you are safe to come to, and perfectly good to me.⟩] MS. *(The letter first ended here but Swinburne crossed out this passage and wrote a new conclusion.)*

Page 133, l. 15: come to. ⟨Write me a word soon, and tell me all you can hear or guess about her; I am never at peace for her now, and⟩] MS.

Page 134, date: ⟨Oct.⟩] MS.

Page 135, l. 12: me. ⟨If I could be the sort of sister that you are he would be a different⟩] MS.

Page 136, date: ⟨Nov.⟩] MS.

Page 136, l. 1: ⟨Dear Audley—Don't get into a state of mind because I'm⟩ I am] MS.

Page 136, l. 5: dropped ⟨writing for the time; and now he says my⟩] MS.

Page 136, l. 9: her: ⟨I don't well believe there are such women yet.⟩] MS.

Page 137, l. 11: head. ⟨Her patience hurts one to see.⟩] MS.

Page 138, ll. 7–8: When she . . . her neck.] *om.* 05.

Page 138, l. 7: see ⟨the purple of a vein⟩] MS.

Page 140, ll. 21–22: *Connu.* "La patrie . . . pommes."] *om.* 05.

Page 141, l. 12: Miss ⟨Herbert⟩] MS.

Page 142, date: ⟨Dec⟩] MS.

Page 142, l. 15: well. I ⟨am not going to begin making lachrymose references to myself. But I am very wretched now, and⟩ want] MS.

Page 143, ll. 6–8: I shall suspect . . . love him.] *om.* 05.

Page 143, l. 28: it would ⟨ruin every one involved⟩] MS.

Page 143, ll. 29–35: Mme de Rochelais . . . letter about you.] *om.* 05.

Page 143, l. 29: says, Elle] says, in what my grandmother calls her new style of sham-imperial slang,—"Elle 77.

Page 143, l. 30: sauter les ⟨amoureux⟩] MS.

Page 144, ll. 11–12: so made up . . . fail one.] *om.* 05.

Page 145, l. 20: crown with. ⟨Oh my darling⟩] MS.

Page 145, l. 22: my love ⟨and own that is now.⟩ ⟨you that are my very own love now.⟩] MS.

Page 145, l. 23: a good bit ⟨first, till the poor Saracen got killed off. If one could turn the best knight now that Iseult has mercy; but you let me in too soon to Joyous Gard⟩; but are you ever going to be afraid of the old king in Cornwall after this?] MS. *(This passage is heavily rewritten—I have omitted deletions within the deleted part.)*

Page 145, ll. 25–26: Tu seras . . . aimerons.] Je serai grand, et toi riche, / Puisque nous nous aimerons. 05. *(This change is not recorded in the 05 proofs.)*

Page 147, ll. 33–34: San ⟨Giovanni-e-Paolo⟩] MS.

Page 153, ll. 17–18: a ⟨British⟩ public] MS.

Page 154, ll. 7–8: I suppose . . . honour.] *om.* 05.

Page 159, l. 8: trouble ⟨or affects any intimacy⟩] MS.

Page 163, l. 5: manner of ⟨their⟩ final ⟨interview. She let him come at their London⟩] MS.

Page 165, close: Explicit.] *om.* 05. *(Not deleted in the 05 proofs.)*

Explanatory Notes

Page 3: *To the Author:* Compare the "Avertissement de l'éditeur" in *Les Liaisons dangereuses* (1782), by Choderlos de Laclos, where the reader is warned by the fictitious publisher that the author "a osé faire paraître sous notre costume et avec nos usages, des mœurs qui nous sont si étrangères."

Page 8, l. 24: *what are the considerations of rhyme and metre to those of matter and meaning?:* Compare *Notes on Poems and Reviews* (1866), where Swinburne, defending his *Poems and Ballads* (1866) against the charge of immorality, argues: "These poems do not seem to me condemnable, unless it be on the ground of bad verse; and to any charge of that kind I should of course be as unable as reluctant to reply."

Page 8, l. 32: *gladiators:* Compare Swinburne's satiric sketch, "M. Prudhomme on Art and Science at the International Exhibition," composed in 1862 but not published by Swinburne (the text is in the "Bonchurch Edition," XV, 399–408): M. Prudhomme (see below, note to p. 119, ll. 3–4) "passed down the gallery of French pictures, bland and merciful; a tear once dimmed those hallowed *besicles* of his, at sight of Mlle. Browne's nursing sisters; his eyelid dropped with disgust, his lip rose and curled with loathing, at sight of the great Gérôme, gladiators not being all that his nervous system could desire." Gérôme's picture, painted in 1859, *Ave Caesar, morituri te salutant* (see the motto of Swinburne's "Faustine," and ll. 233–248 of "Dolores"), was praised by Gautier. It is now at the Yale University Art Gallery. See the catalogue of an exhibit of 1972–1973, *Jean-Léon Gérôme (1824–1904)*, organized by Bruce H. Evans, introduction by Gerald M. Ackerman, essay by Richard Ettinghausen. On Henriette Brown (Mme Jules de Saux) and her pictures at the 1862 Exhibition, see the review in *The Times,* July 14, 1862, p. 7, in which three columns are devoted to the French pictures without mentioning Gérôme, whose gladiators the reviewer evidently thought "better forgotten."

Page 9, l. 31: *Rosette et Rosine, Confidences d'un Fauteuil:* The first title suggests Sade's *Justine* (1791) and *Juliette* (1798). The second recalls Crébillon's *Le Sopha* (1740); and a novel (attributed to Alfred Sirven) called *Les*

Confidences d'un canapé (Paris, 1862). Swinburne refers to "the pseudony-
mous authoress of *Rosine et Rosette, Confidences d'un Fauteuil,* and other
books of as questionable a kind," in his burlesque review of "Les Abîmes,
Par Ernest Clouët," in *New Writings by Swinburne*, edited by C. Y. Lang
(Syracuse, N. Y., 1964), p. 102.

Page 11, l. 8: *Reginald-Edward, born April 7ᵗʰ 1838:* Swinburne was born on
April 5, 1837. His mother's family (Ashburnham) traced its name to
Reginald de Oseburnham, who was extant in 1166; Swinburne's uncle,
Reginald Ashburnham (b. 1819), had died in 1830. His great-grandfather
was Edward Swinburne (5th Baronet), and the poet's brother was named
Edward.

Page 15, l. 25: *instances of a like taste:* The reference is to the "philosophy" of
the marquis de Sade.

Page 18, l. 29: *Lidcombe:* Compare this description with that by Swinburne's
cousin, Mary Gordon (Mrs. Disney Leith), of Capheaton, the seat of the
Swinburne family: "A large cousinhood gathered there in those bright
autumn days, where everything seemed to combine for the delight of
youth—a lake to row or sail on, lovely gardens and woods to roam or play in,
and, above all, abundance of ponies to ride"; *The Boyhood of Algernon
Charles Swinburne: Personal Recollections by his Cousin* (London, 1917), p.
11. There is a picture of Capheaton (reproduced above, on p. xiii) by Miss
E. Swinburne, one of Algernon's aunts, in J. P. Neale's *Views of the Seats of
Noblemen and Gentlemen* (London, 1822), vol. I, unpaged.

Page 20, l. 16: *muscle-manful type:* Compare "M. Prudhomme": "The Rugby
and muscular-Christian schools have pretty well infected the very race of
boys with Prudhomme views—exquisite Prudhomme sentiment and 'godly,
manly' Prudhomme religion. . . . could not the poor boy have been left at
peace in his quiet honest animal condition?" See below, Captain
Harewood's letter to Reginald.

Page 22, l. 34: *Pepperbottom, that was out of a book:* Perhaps Swinburne's own
(unpublished) book, *The Flogging-Block* (MS. Ashley 5256). In "Eclogue
II: Reginald's Flogging," the Master says to Redgie: "You are nicknamed,
I hear, in the lower division, / Pepperbottom—a term of appropriate
derision." Compare: "My master pepered my ars with well good spede,"
from "The Birched School-Boy," in *Early English Meals and Manners,*

[180]

edited by F. J. Furnivall, Early English Text Society, Original Series, 32 (London, 1868), p. 386.

Page 24, l. 24: *affair of honour:* In *Lesbia Brandon,* the narrator says of Herbert: "it had grown into a point of honour with him to take what fate sent him at his tutor's hands with a rebellious reticence, and bear anything in reason rather than expose himself to an intercession which he could not but imagine contemptuous; and thus every flogging became a duel without seconds between the man and the boy" (edited by Randolph Hughes, p. 17). Compare the following passage from the "Prelude to Charlie's Flogging," in *The Flogging-Block:*

>   . . . I don't think Algy Clavering the worst
> Of the boys we have here to look after—he's brave
> And honest and generous; but then such a slave
> To each whim of the moment—the wind and the wave
> Are steady, compared to that youngster: and yet
> There are times, now and then, when I really regret
> To remember how often I've flogged him, and think
> How often again I must flog him. I'd wink
> If I could, at his faults now and then: but I fear
> He's proud of the fact that no other boy here
> Gets punished as often as he—which is clearly
> The fact—and no other gets flogged so severely.

Page 24, l. 30: *Orbilius:* The severe (*plagosus*) teacher of the poet Horace (*Epistles*, II. i. 71).

Page 25, l. 12: *The trodden worm turned and stung:* Proverbial; see the *Oxford English Dictionary* under "worm," sec. 3b.

Page 26, l. 12: *the voice of the officiating master:* As in *The Flogging-Block,* "Willie's Flogging": "Does it hurt? (whipping Willie) does it hurt you, my lad? / I'm glad that you feel it (whipping Willie again)—I'm heartily glad. 5 cuts."

Page 27, l. 3: *"lowly and serviceable":* Like the Squire in Chaucer's *Canterbury Tales,* "General Prologue," l. 99.

Page 30, l. 3: *not much else to say:* At this point it may be helpful to summarize the family history:

1. LORD CHEYNE, of Lidcombe (*d.* July 1858), *m.* (his wife *d.* 1830), and had one son,

   EDMUND, *b.* 1830 (*d.* 1861), *m.* May 1859, his cousin, Amicia, da. of Frederick Stanford.

2. JOHN, *b. ca.* 1795 (*d.* 1857), *m.* Miss Banks (*d.* 1841), by whom he had issue,

   1. CLARA, *b.* 1836, *m.* 1855 Ernest Radworth, of Blocksham, *b.* 1833.
   2. FRANCIS, *b.* 1840.

3. HELENA, *b.* March 1800, *m.* 1819 Sir Thomas Midhurst, Bart. *(dec'd)* and had one daughter,

   AMICIA, *b.* 1820, *m.* first in May 1837 Captain Philip Harewood, of Plessey, by whom she had issue,

   1. REGINALD-EDWARD, *b.* April 7, 1838.

   This marriage was dissolved in 1840; she *m.* second in 1840 Frederick Stanford Esq. of Ashton Hildred, co. Bucks, by whom she had issue,

   2. AMICIA, *b.* May 1841, *m.* May 1859 her cousin, Edmund Cheyne.

Page 30, l. 15: *the untimely plough:* To be "ploughed" is the Oxford equivalent of to be "failed in one's examinations." Swinburne himself failed his "first examination in Classics" in late 1859; he spent the winter being coached to take examinations in the spring of 1860. But he fell from a horse and got badly cut up just before the date arrived. Whether he took them and failed, or whether his studies were terminated for some other reason, is not certain. See Lafourcade, *La Jeunesse*, I, 166–167; *Letters*, I, 26–36.

Page 32, l. 16: *Madame de Léry in Un Caprice:* The witty, charming, seductive heroine of Musset's play (1837).

Page 35, l. 18: *soft suggestive Iago style:* As in Act III, scene iii of *Othello*.

Page 38, l. 3: *a French novel and a Dickens nurse:* Swinburne's deleted words "—Feydeau plus Gamp" suggest what sort of French novel Clara had in mind; see below, note to p. 154, l. 7. Swinburne's change in 1877 from "novel" to "portière" suggests that he saw a better parallel in Mme Pipelet, in *Les Mystères de Paris* (1843–1844), by Eugène Süe; see part I, ch. xxiii. Mrs. Gamp appears in *Martin Chuzzlewit* (1844). Swinburne refers to her constantly in his letters. See also his *Charles Dickens* (1913), pp. 27–29.

Page 42, l. 3: *all out of spite to his mother and me:* Compare p. 15, l. 32 and p. 162, ll. 26–27. In *Lesbia Brandon* Denham flogs Bertie all the more viciously because of his helpless love for his victim's sister.

Page 42, l. 33: *Balzac:* Lady Midhurst is doubtless thinking of Mme Marneffe, the brilliantly immoral manager of amatory intrigues in *La Cousine Bette* (1847), whom Swinburne in 1861 acclaimed as "the greatest of her sex and an honour to humanity" (*Letters*, I, 43).

Page 43, l. 15: *the game:* "English billiards," in which one scores by making cannons with the three balls, or by pocketing them.

Page 45, l. 5: *duc de Beaulnes:* Swinburne originally wrote "Chaulnes," which is the name of an old Parisian family. See the articles in the *Dictionnaire de biographie française*, sous la direction de M. Prévost et Roman d'Amat (1959), vol. VIII. Hugo, in *Les Contemplations*, V. III. i, remembers "Les paysans pendus par ce bon duc de Chaulnes."

Page 45, l. 11: *M. de S∗∗∗:* That is, the unutterable name of the "divine" marquis de Sade.

Page 45, l. 18: *Mme de Phalaris:* Or Falari, mistress of Philippe II d' Orléans (1674–1723), regent during the minority of Louis XV; she is mentioned in the *Mémoires* of the duc de Saint-Simon; nothing is known of her after the death of her protector.

Page 45, l. 23: *Eisen:* Charles Dominique Joseph Eisen (1720–1778), illustrator of La Fontaine and of Ovid, and a favorite of Mme de Pompadour. His delicately drawn "gravures galantes" decorated the pages of many other works, including novels by F. T. M. Baculard d'Arnaud, such as *Fanni, ou La nouvelle Paméla, histoire anglaise* (1767), *Julie, ou l'heureux repentir* (1767), and *Nancy, ou les malheurs de l'imprudence, et de la jalousie* (1767).

Page 45, l. 30: *Mme de Montreuil:* Sade's mother-in-law. "Madame la présidente" appears in *Les Liaisons dangereuses.* It is not surprising that Lady Midhurst should have chosen Mme de Montreuil as a model; their characters are altogether sympathetic. The following description could serve equally for either one: elle "se décide et agit avec tous les préjugés de sa caste, mais elle domine les motifs qui la poussent. Elle fait le nécessaire pour aboutir et ne s'embarrasse jamais des droits et des peines d'autrui. . . . Tout est présent à son esprit à l'heure qu'il faut et elle n'a jamais à se repentir d'un échec ou à chercher un responsable. Le passé ne compte plus à ses yeux. Elle est sans regrets comme sans remords." P. Bourdin, introduction, *Correspondance inéditée du marquis de Sade* (Paris, 1929), pp. xxx–xxxii; quoted by Gilbert Lély, *Vie du marquis de Sade,* in *Œuvres complètes du marquis de Sade,* édition définitive (Paris, 1966), I, 79–80.

Page 46, l. 23: *the other name:* Perhaps *Justine?*

Page 51, l. 5: *Garibaldi and the Sicilian business:* Garibaldi and "the thousand" landed at Marsala in May 1860. Swinburne was by 1858 a passionate adherent of the Italian cause; see his poems "Ode to Mazzini," "The Temple of Janus," and his essay "On Foreign Intervention" (the first in "Bonchurch" and extracts from the last two in Lafourcade, *La Jeunesse,* II, 17–18, 209–217). In 1858, with an Oxford friend, John Nichol, he subscribed the formidable sum of £100 to the "Partito d'Azione," sponsored by Mazzini and Aurelio Saffi (who was Swinburne's teacher at Oxford); see *Scritti editi ed inediti di Giuseppe Mazzini,* edizione ʻnazionale (Imola, 1908–1943), LX (*Epistolario,* XXXV) (1931), 96; see also pp. 282–283, and 301.

Page 51, l. 17: *the Roman question:* The question of the temporal power of the Pope, who ruled Rome till 1870, and was the last obstacle in the way of Italian unification.

Page 52, l. 14: *hair on your lips and chin:* Like Redgie, Swinburne had an unusually delicate complexion, and (in 1862) the wispiest of whiskers (see Lafourcade, *La Jeunesse,* I, plates IV–VIII). By 1905, when he deleted this passage, time had amended the defect; see Clara Watts-Dunton, *The Home Life of Swinburne* (London, 1922), frontispiece.

Page 52, l. 16: *lower fifth:* At this stage in his Eton career, Swinburne was thirteen years old (Lafourcade, *La Jeunesse,* I, 82–83).

Page 52, l. 20: *hairbrained:* This spelling is not unusual among nineteenth-century writers (see *OED*).

Page 52, l. 24: *chouse:* "From ca. 1850 at Eton": "a shame, as in 'a beastly chouse,' or an imposition"; Eric Partridge, *A Dictionary of Slang and Unconventional English*, 7th ed. (New York, 1970).

Page 53, l. 24: *Dr. Birkenshaw:* The name literally means "birch-grove." He is the headmaster of Much Birchingham School, Rodbury, Northumberland, where the scenes of *The Flogging-Block* take place.

Page 55, l. 7: *neptiphobia:* Latin "neptis" (here meaning "niece") and the Greek suffix "-phobia." The mixed word is "barbaric," that is, not Greek.

Page 55, ll. 19–22: *Murillo . . . Callot:* Lady Midhurst is thinking of pictures of wide-eyed beggar boys by Murillo (1617–1682); more acceptable, because less tainted by sentiment, are satirical sporting drawings for *Punch* by John Leech (1817–1864); and engravings of grotesque figures by Callot (1592–1635).

Page 55, l. 31: *St. Agnes:* A virtuous maiden of the time of Diocletian, martyred for her unwillingness to compromise her religion or her purity.

Page 56, ll. 7–9: *off with her . . . on with her:* Compare: "It is best to be off wi' the old love / Before you be on wi' the new" in Scott's *The Bride of Lammermoor,* ch. xxix.

Page 56, l. 15: *Queen of Sheba:* She married King Solomon out of admiration for his wisdom (I. Kings x. 1–13).

Page 56, l. 26: *Egyptian plague:* Clara has her "fun" like Jehovah, who brought down blood, frogs, lice, flies, murrain, boils, hail, locusts, darkness, and death to the firstborn—all to show the Egyptians how powerful he was (Exodus vii–xii).

Page 56, l. 29: *the Garden:* The Garden of Epicurus, where he taught his pupils.

Page 56, l. 30: *the strait gate:* "Enter ye in at the strait gate: for wide is the gate, and broad is the way, that leadeth to destruction" (Matthew vii. 13).

Page 57, ll. 2–3: *Athénaïs de Montespan . . . Louise de la Vallière:* Mistresses of Louis XIV: the first (1641–1707), beautiful, brilliant, scheming; the second (1644–1710), gentle, sincere, artless—Mme de Sévigné called her "cette petite *violette qui se cachoit sous l'herbe* et qui étoit honteuse d'être maîtresse, d'être mère, d'être duchesse: jamais il n'y en aura sur ce moule" (à Mme de Grignan, 1ᵉʳ septembre 1680).

Page 57, l. 28: *Elizabeth:* Mary Stuart (1542–1587) pursued her aims and her passions at once recklessly and skillfully. See (if you have time) Swinburne's immense dramatic trilogy, *Chastelard* (1865), *Bothwell* (1874), and *Mary Stuart* (1881); and his article on her in the *Encyclopædia Britannica*, 9th edition (1883). Elizabeth (1533–1603) was more prudent and politic than Mary: Leicester (1532?–1588) managed to keep her favor and his place, but Essex (1566–1601) was "impulsive as a schoolboy" (*DNB*), and ruined himself. Clara is not *that* much older than Redgie.

Page 58, l. 6: *liberavi animam meam:* Proverbial: the words are originally St. Bernard's (Epistle 371); the sense is "I have discharged my conscience." Compare *Letters,* V, 98.

Page 59, l. 13: *Hadleigh:* There is a place by that name in Essex, but Swinburne is not necessarily referring to it; he is certainly remembering moments such as inspired the concluding lines of "Hesperia" in *Poems and Ballads.*

Page 59, l. 27: *Nourmahal:* The Sultana Nourmahal, whose name means "The Light of the Haram," appears in Thomas Moore's *Lalla Rookh* (1817); but Swinburne is likely to have been more impressed by the gentle but dangerous "Nourmahal-la-Rousse" in Hugo's *Les Orientales* (1829).

Page 61, l. 5: *Portsmouth:* Across from the Isle of Wight, opposite Ryde.

Page 68, l. 14: *Rigolboche:* Stage name of a "danseuse excentrique," Marguerite Badel, who attained a certain fame from 1855 to 1860; see the spirited *Mémoires de Rigolboche, ornés d'un portrait photographié par Petit et Trinquart* [attributed to Ernest Blum], 6th ed. (Paris, 1860). A copy at Harvard has a learned MS. note on the title-page: "She was a 'can-can' dancer; and the first of the 'high-kickers.' " The lines which Swinburne added in his note of 1877 are from Villon's "Ballade des dames du temps jadis."

Page 68, l. 15: *similies:* An old-fashioned spelling (see *OED*).

Page 68, l. 22: *quadrilateral:* "The space lying between, and defended by, four fortresses; *spec.* that in North Italy formed by the fortresses of Mantua, Verona, Peschiera, and Legnano" (*OED*).

Page 68, l. 23: *picciotti:* The Sicilians who joined Garibaldi in 1860.

Page 69, l. 2: *mad martyr:* See the lively watercolor (1861) by Lady Pauline Jermyn Trevelyan (who may have modelled to some degree for Swinburne's literary portrait of Lady Midhurst): "A. C. S. sent to the guillotine by order of Louis Napoleon addresses the people"; reproduced on the cover of *Swinburneiana: A Gallimaufry of Bits and Pieces about Algernon Charles Swinburne*, written and edited by John S. Mayfield (1974).

Page 69, l. 3: *Committees of Public Safety:* Like the one of 1793, which carried on the "Reign of Terror."

Page 69, l. 11: *"J'ai connu des vivants à qui Danton parlait":* I cannot locate this verse in Hugo's poems. But the fact is attested of him in a note to *Quatrevingt-treize* (1874), in which he tells of the abbé who performed Danton's marriage, and who "m'a souvent dit la messe en 1815, 1816, 1817, 1818"; in *Œuvres complètes*, édition de l'Imprimerie Nationale (Paris, 1904–1952), Roman, IX (1924), 388.

Page 71, l. 2: *Diana:* The pure-spirited huntress made Actaeon sprout a pair of stag's horns (Ovid, *Metamorphoses,* III. 138 ff.); see below, note to p. 73, l. 3.

Page 72, l. 34: *heartsickness:* The French sense, as in *avoir mal au cœur,* "to feel sick."

Page 73, l. 3: *fœnum habet:* Ernest with horns again, this time like a dangerous ox, which "has hay" tied on one horn as a warning (Horace, *Satires,* I. iv. 34).

Page 78, l. 14: *Sand:* George Sand (1804–1876), novelist, lover of men, defender of women.

Page 78, l. 24: *"out of the sad unmerciful sea":* Clara compares herself to Andromeda (Ovid, *Metamorphoses,* IV. 663 ff.).

Page 80, ll. 19–20: *Chalfont's Essays:* He and his book appear to be inventions

[187]

of Swinburne's; but the tone and style faintly suggest Carlyle's *Past and Present* (1843).

Page 82, l. 8: *Aboulfadir:* This wise man of the East is apparently Swinburne's creation, but the quotation has a hint of Omar about it (Swinburne had read the *Rubaiyat* within a year or two of its appearance in 1859). Compare also "Before the beginning of years," in *Atalanta in Calydon.*

Page 83, l. 15: *the sea as a profession:* Swinburne's father was an admiral; whether Algernon had ever been destined for the navy is not known. He did want to join the army, but his father decided against it (see *Letters,* VI, 251), and therefore sent him to Oxford to prepare for the law or the Church. See below, p. 121, ll. 11–14, and p. 161, ll. 25–28.

Page 86, l. 14: *"selfless and stainless":* Words applied to King Arthur in Tennyson's *Idylls* (1859), "Merlin and Vivien," l. 790. Swinburne's unflattering opinion of the *Idylls* is expressed in (for example) *Under the Microscope* (1872), pp. 36–45.

Page 88, l. 10: *"salad days":* Antony and Cleopatra, I. v. 73.

Page 90, l. 19: *Musset:* The lines are from "Les Marrons du feu," scène v, in *Contes d'Espagne et d'Italie* (1830).

Page 91, l. 23: *"chew the thrice-turned cud of wrath":* Tennyson, *The Princess* (1847), I. 64–65.

Page 94, l. 11: *put away from him:* The language echoes Matthew v. 32; the one offence which would justify this was fornication.

Page 97, l. 14: *overfalls:* "A turbulent surface of water with short breaking waves, caused by a strong current or tide setting over a submarine ridge or shoal, or by the meeting of contrary currents" (*OED*).

Page 97, l. 29: *groundswell:* "A deep swell or heavy rolling of the sea" (*OED*).

Page 103, l. 13: *"free-will offering":* Words from Psalm cxix. 108.

Page 108, l. 3: *carte de visite:* One with a small photograph on it, such as Swinburne used to give to admirers. There is a copy (see above, frontispiece) in the Harvard College Library with Swinburne's letter from Aberystwith [ca. October 27, 1866] to F. G. Waugh.

Page 110, l. 25: *of every day:* The construction is analogous to "of an evening" (see *OED*, under "of," sec. XV).

Page 112, l. 30: *why Courbet?:* Perhaps because of the assertive bohemianism of the French painter (1819–1877).

Page 113, l. 1: *"William, tenth baron":* The fictional family of Swinburne's novel is of unusually ancient and continuous lineage, since the title would have been created around 1300. The story may be an authentic episode from Swinburne's family tradition (see *Letters*, III, 252). His ancestor, William Swinburne (d. 1653), was first married to "Margaret, eldest sister, and at length sole heiress of Sir Thomas Swinburne of Edlingham, Northumberland"; see *Burke's Genealogical and Heraldic History of the Peerage, Baronetage, and Knightage*, edited by Peter Townend, 104th edition (London, 1967), p. 2434.

Page 113, l. 7: *Herbert Society:* Swinburne wrote "Wardour," then "Carew" (whose style the poem imitates), before settling on the pleasantly incongruous name of the devout George Herbert.

Page 113, l. 21: *a maze:* An obsolete equivalent of "bewilderment" (*OED*).

Page 114, l. 10: *Naseby:* Where Cromwell defeated the Royalists on June 14, 1645.

Page 114, l. 13: *"never had any great joy of his life afterwards":* The phrase is a variation of the stock conclusion to the sort of renaissance tale that Swinburne is here imitating in both subject and style. Compare his other attempts in the genre, such as "Dead Love," or "The Chronicle of Queen Fredegond," and others discussed by Lafourcade, *La Jeunesse*, II, 73–93.

Page 116, l. 26: *Prodgers:* This author, and his book on the science of all things, appear to be inventions of Swinburne's.

Page 117, l. 8: *Mme Mario:* Jesse White Mario (1832–1906) "did her best to be the Florence Nightingale" of Garibaldi's campaign of 1860; G. M. Trevelyan, *Garibaldi and the Making of Italy* (London, 1911), p. 97.

Page 117, l. 9: *Cavour:* He died on June 6, 1861. Redgie's tone of reservation is understandable in light of his revolutionary sympathies: Cavour was neither a hero (like Garibaldi), nor a prophet (like Mazzini), but a politician, who was not unwilling to support King Victor Emmanuel to achieve his goal of a unified Italy.

Page 117, ll. 14–17: *"piteous ruinous beauty . . . sunset":* The words may be Swinburne's own. He first visited Venice in the early months of 1861 (see *Letters,* I, 39, 43; Lafourcade, *La Jeunesse,* I, 187–188).

Page 117, l. 18: *days'-work:* Thus in Swinburne's MS., instead of the usual *day's-work.*

Page 118, l. 5: *"from the lily-leaf to the lily-stem":* The diction, meter, and rhyme, are typical of Swinburne's verse, especially in *Poems and Ballads,* where he rhymes "flame" (one of his favorite rhyme words) and "them" in "Laus Veneris" and in "Anactoria."

Page 119, ll. 3–4: *Prudhomme Coquardeau:* Two humorous philistines who figure in Swinburne's "M. Prudhomme." M. Prudhomme was the literary and artistic creation of Henri Monnier (1805–1877). A play titled *Coquardeau et compagnie,* by Émile Thierry and Eugène Moniot was performed at the Théâtre Déjazet on April 7, 1861; listed in Charles Beaumont Wicks, *The Parisian Stage, Part IV (1851–1875)* (University, Alabama, 1967), entry no. 15927. Gavarni (pen name of S-G. Chevalier, 1804–1866), was a prolific illustrator and caricaturist.

Page 119, l. 17: *Paul et Virginie:* The characters and title of a sentimental novel (1788) by Bernardin de Saint-Pierre (1737–1814).

Page 119, l. 19: *table of affinities:* At the back of the Book of Common Prayer, following the thirty-nine articles, is "A Table of Kindred and Affinity, Wherein whosoever are related are forbidden in Scripture and our Laws to marry together." See below, note to p. 154, l. 4.

Page 119, l. 26: *Valfons, Lauzun, Richelieu's own self:* Types of the courtier: Valfons (1710–1786) was favored by Louis XV—his *Souvenirs* were published in Paris in 1860; Lauzun (1632–1723) was a favorite of Louis XIV; Richelieu (1585–1642) dominated the reign of Louis XIII.

Page 119, l. 29: *Ce nom tramontain:* Philomena was the name of the supposed virgin and martyr of the third century whose bones were discovered in 1802. In 1855 the Curé of Ars "moved the Congregation of Rites to institute a Mass and an Office of St. Philomena"; but she has since (1961) been removed from the list of saints (*New Catholic Encyclopedia,* 1967). The form "tramontain" is a variant of the usual "ultramontain."

Page 120, l. 10: *the directory:* The period from 1795 to 1799, when France was governed by a board of "directors."

Page 120, l. 17: *"La Femme de Cinquante Ans, Étude":* The title and subtitle suggest the novels of Ernest Feydeau. See below, note to p. 154, l. 7.

Page 120, l. 17: *Jules de Versac:* In Crébillon's novel, *Les Égarements du cœur et de l'esprit* (1736), there is "un impudent précepteur du vice" named Versac, who may have served as a model for Valmont in *Les Liaisons dangereuses.*

Page 121, l. 17: *Prince Metternich:* The Austrian statesman (1773–1859), whose eighteenth-century style and talent for brilliant intrigue would have sufficiently endeared him to Lady Midhurst.

Page 121, l. 23: *windmill:* An obsolete usage: "A fanciful notion, a crotchet; a visionary scheme or project" (*OED*).

Page 122, l. 10: *legitimist:* A supporter of the comte de Chambord, "Henri V" (1820–1883), as heir in the Bourbon line to the French throne. In 1859 he joined forces with the Church. The lily was a device of the French monarchy. The "old standard" was the white flag of the Bourbons.

Page 122, l. 19: *Sultan Mourad's pig:* In *La Légende des siècles* (1859), XVI. III. iv. 225.

Page 123, l. 4: *"shaken and sounded through by the trumpets of the sea":* Compare the last lines of "Laus Veneris": "Until God loosen over sea and land / The thunder of the trumpets of the night."

Page 123, l. 24: *Thebaid:* The title of an epic poem by Statius, on the quarrel between Eteocles and Polynices, sons of Oedipus, brothers of Antigone.

Page 127, ll. 31–32: *To himself he has been . . . true:* An echo of Polonius, in *Hamlet,* I. iii. 78.

[191]

Page 130, l. 22: *a face ten times more beautiful:* Oswald Doughty suggested that this description was based on Swinburne's impressions of Rossetti's wife, Lizzie Siddal; *A Victorian Romantic: Dante Gabriel Rossetti* (London, 1949), pp. 274, 683n.

Page 135, l. 17: *a painful hearing:* Compare Dickens, *Barnaby Rudge,* ch. xlviii: "This is a pleasant hearing" (cited in *OED*).

Page 136, l. 2: *my father:* In his outline for the novel, Swinburne characterized this letter as "style Cecco." Cecco Angiolieri was a contemporary of Dante, of whom D. G. Rossetti wrote in the introduction to *Dante and his Circle* (1861): "Nearly all his sonnets (and no other pieces by him have been preserved) relate either to an unnatural hatred of his father, or to an infatuated love for the daughter of a shoemaker, a certain married Becchina." In a letter of February 22, 1870, Swinburne referred to Cecco as his "Sienese predecessor."

Page 137, l. 10: *Haynau:* Austrian general (1786–1853), notorious for his cruelty to the Italians.

Page 138, l. 28: *she always rather hated Frank and me:* Clara was echoing her brother; compare p. 133, ll. 4–5.

Page 139, l. 21: *Stendhal: La Chartreuse de Parme* (1839), by Stendhal (pseudonym of Henri Beyle, 1783–1842). The hero, Fabrice del Dongo, whose most ardent protector is his aunt, resembles Redgie in his reckless enthusiasm for adventure and for "la chasse de l'amour" (ch. xiv).

Page 140, l. 9: *Pius-Iscariot:* Swinburne used a similar epithet for Pope Pius IX; see "Peter's Pence from Perugia," and "Papal Allocution" (1873) in *Diræ,* Swinburne's attempt in the manner of Hugo's *Les Châtiments* (1853).

Page 140, l. 10: *Gaeta:* A coastal fortress above Naples, where the Bourbons were defeated in 1861.

Page 140, l. 11: *men of December:* Supporters of Napoleon III, who proclaimed the Second Empire in December 1852 (see *Letters,* II, 85–86).

Page 140, l. 13: *volunteer bayonets:* The British volunteer corps of 1859, drawn up at the moment of a French war scare (see *Letters,* I, 29).

Page 140, l. 15: *the Beauharnais:* That is, the son of Hortense de Beauharnais, Napoleon III, whose right to the name "Bonaparte" was doubted in certain quarters (see *Letters*, I, 29). The epithet was used by Hugo in *Les Châtiments*, e.g. VI. xi: "Bonaparte apocryphe, / A coup sûr Beauharnais, peut-être Verhuell."

Page 140, l. 18: *the society that was saved:* Napoleon III was hailed by his supporters as "The Saviour of Society"; see Swinburne's sonnets of the same title (1873) in *Diræ*, and his letter of 1873 to the *Examiner* (in *Letters*, II, 246–250). Compare *Les Châtiments*, VII: "Les Sauveurs se sauveront."

Page 140, l. 22: *MM. les doctrinaires:* Advocates of the *juste-milieu* between democracy and monarchy.

Page 141, l. 12: *Victor Hugo:* Signs of Swinburne's Hugolatry may be found throughout his poems, dramas, and criticism. See especially his *Study of Victor Hugo* (1886).

Page 141, l. 12: *A fellow who rode in the Balaklava charge:* Swinburne during his trip to Europe in 1855 met a soldier who had been at Balaklava (*Letters*, I, 5). Of Swinburne's wish, at the age of seventeen, to enter the army, he wrote: "The Balaklava charge eclipsed all other visions" (*Letters*, VI, 251). The charge took place on October 25, 1854.

Page 145, l. 23: *play Palomydes to your Iseult:* In the Tristram story, Palomydes is a minstrel who visits King Mark's court in Cornwall and, taking the king at his word when he offers a boon, asks for, and receives, Iseult. After they leave, Tristram pursues them, kills Palomydes, and rescues Iseult. See Swinburne's version of the story in his *Tristram of Lyonesse* (1882).

Page 145, ll. 25–26: *Tu seras dame . . . aimerons:* Swinburne, in his revision of 1905, corrected this fusion of two separate lines from a song in the story of Eviradnus in Hugo's *La Légende des siècles* (1859), XV. iii. xi. Compare the comments on these lines in Swinburne's *Study of Victor Hugo*, pp. 115–116.

Page 147, l. 34: *San Zanipolo:* The Venetian name for the basilica of San Giovanni e Paolo. The picture (reproduced above, on p. xv), now attributed not to Carpaccio, but to the school of Cima da Conegliano, is commented on by F. Z. Boccazzi, *La Basilica dei Santi Giovanni e Paolo in Venezia* (1965), fig. 94, p. 163. On Swinburne's acquaintance with Carpaccio, see *Letters*, I,

92, where he mentions pictures by him at the Academy in Venice, and at Brescia.

Page 149, l. 23: *la dame aux belles cousines:* In *Le Petit Jehan de Saintré* by Antoine de la Sale (1385/6–after 1460); she instructs Jehan in the arts of love and gentlemanly conduct; when he goes off on knightly adventures, she takes up with a lecherous Abbé. The suggested analogies between Armande and "la dame," between Jehan and John Cheyne, and perhaps between the Abbé and Fabien de Rochelais, form an unwritten episode to the novel.

Page 150, l. 9: *halve the charge:* To divide a shield so that the arms of two allied families may be shown at once.

Page 151, l. 25: *Madame Bovary:* Rodolphe, Emma's first lover, "avait trente-quatre ans; il était de tempérament brutal et d'intelligence perspicace, ayant d'ailleurs beaucoup fréquenté les femmes et s'y connaissant bien" (II. vii). He possessed a marvelous accumulation of old garters, locks of hair, and, especially, letters—which he regarded as a "tas de blagues" (II. xiii). *Madame Bovary* first appeared in the *Revue de Paris* in 1856, and came out as a book in 1857.

Page 153, l. 16: *Iphigenia:* She was offered as a sacrifice by her father, Agammenon, so as to arouse the winds that would take his fleet to Troy.

Page 153, l. 19: *"a fool of his folly":* Compare Proverbs xxvi. 5, 11.

Page 154, l. 4: *the canon of our church about men's grandmothers:* "A man may not marry his Grandmother" was the first item in the "Table of Kindred and Affinity." See above, note to p. 119, l. 19.

Page 154, l. 7: *M. Feydeau:* Ernest Feydeau (1821–1873); his first novel, *Fanny, étude* (1858), made a great effect on account of its sensational representation of an adulterous love affair. He followed up this success with *Daniel, étude* (1859), *Catherine d'Overmeire, étude* (1860), *Sylvie, étude* (1861), and many others—all daring in their curious psychological explorations. A grandmother plays a prominent role in *Catherine d'Overmeire.*

Page 154, l. 8: *Ninon:* Ninon de Lenclos (1620–1705), whose inexhaustible attractions drew to her an astoundingly long series of illustrious lovers. But

[194]

it is doubtful whether a grandson of hers was among the suitors of her sunset years.

Page 155, l. 35: *Love and Age:* Peacock's novel, *Gryll Grange*, first appeared serially in *Fraser's Magazine* (April–December 1860); the book came out in 1861. Lady Midhurst's memory is accurate: "Love and Age" was in the July issue (vol. 62, pp. 49–50).

Page 156, l. 23: *a case of girl's head and fish's tail:* Horace, *Ars Poetica,* ll. 3–5.

Page 156, l. 28: *Le dénouement:* Compare the epilogue to *Eugénie Grandet* (1833): "Ce dénoûment trompe nécessairement la curiosité. Peut-être en est-il ainsi de tous les dénoûments vrais. Les tragédies, les drames, pour parler le langage de ce temps, sont rares dans la nature."

Page 161, l. 11: *leaven her dead lump:* An echo of St. Paul, I. Corinthians v. 6; Galatians v. 9.

Page 163, l. 23: *Nemesis:* The Greek goddess of vengeance.

Page 165, l. 16: *sinecure—or demi-cure:* A "sinecure" is literally a task without (*sine*) toil (*cura*).

Page 165, l. 25: *Explicit:* The conventional close of medieval and renaissance poems and tales, meaning, *the book is ended.*